MW00657618

FLYING BLUE TACOS

~A COLLECTION OF STORIES~

HECTOR G. GONZALEZ

GUAPO MONKEY PRESS

Copyright © 2014 by Hector Gonzalez

Fifth Printing 2017

Cover Design © 2014 by Lude Graphics

ISBN 978-0-9913335-4-7

Printed in the United States of America

a b c d e f g h I j k...

Contact Information:

Guapo Monkey Press

PO BOX 801

Brea, CA 92835

flyingbluetacos@roadrunner.com

Diego and Elyse:

Never talk yourself out

of pursuing your passions

Flying Blue Tacos

~A Collection of Stories~

FLYING BLUE TACOS

"No, man, *I'm Mexican,"* I answered the guy asking me if I was Greek.

I'm light skinned, so I've been called everything from Italian to French, German, and even Americano by my fellow Mexicanos. So being asked if I was Greek didn't surprise me at all.

I knew what he meant, though. He wasn't asking about my nationality—he was wearing a blue shirt with Alpha Delta Gamma written in gold, and he wanted to know if I was in a Greek fraternity.

The guy gave me a confused look. I continued.

"My name *is* Hector, but *I'm not* Greek."

He still didn't understand that I was messing around with him. I waited a few seconds for him to realize that I was referring to Hector, the Trojan warrior from Greek mythology, but that moment never came.

"I mean, are you in a Greek fraternity?" he asked.

"No, I'm in a Chinese fraternity."

"Really?"

"Yeah, it's called, *Ya No Chingues (stop screwing around)."*

I said it really fast so it'd sound somewhat Chinese. I guess he understood Spanish, though, because he flipped me off and walked away.

As I entered the elevator and headed up to meet my friends in the study room, I was thinking that maybe I should've cut "frat-boy" some slack, because I realize that a Trojan warrior

9

doesn't immediately come to mind upon hearing the name "Hector."

Thanks to movies and television shows, my name is usually associated with janitors, criminals, and gardeners. And whenever there's a scene with a pervert stalking the neighborhood or a fat cat sitting on a couch, his name is usually "Hector." For example...

"Hector, there's a clean-up on aisle five."

"Hector! Hector! Dude, I think your fat-ass cat died!"

"Hector, the alleged stalker who has been mugging elderly women who walk with a limp, has been arrested—again."

Despite all of the negative stereotypes associated with my first name, it's still better than going by my middle name: *Guadalupe*.

God gave me a healthy body and mind, but my parents tainted it all by giving me messed-up names.

I was on my way to the study room to see if anybody else was going to be entering the art contest. Dr. Padilla, the new art professor at Cal State Fullerton, is organizing the contest. Dr. Padilla wants to tap into the "undiscovered artistic talent" among the Mexican-American students at Cal State Fullerton. The prize is $1,000 for first place and $500 for second place. "Our Community" is the theme of the contest, and there're only two requirements to enter-

First, those entering the contest can't be art majors. I'm not.

Second, one has to be Mexican-American. I am.

Well, the application doesn't state if one has to be an American citizen of Mexican descent to enter the contest, or if having a Green Card is good enough. I didn't see anything asking for my Alien Registration Number on the application, so I assumed I was good to go.

To be honest, I wish there were some restrictions against allowing illegal aliens from entering the contest. I know one illegal, Armando Marquez from Zacatecas, who could easily win the whole thing.

Armando is a political science major, of course—or is it ironic? Either way, he works at a tattoo shop on Harbor Boulevard and could easily make the transition from painting on skin to painting on a canvas. So if there were restrictions, Armando and other illegals wouldn't be able to enter the contest, thus giving me a better chance at winning some money.

Just the thought of Armando entering the contest allowed me to empathize for a second with all of the unemployed white construction workers.

I have a feeling someday an unemployed white guy who lost his job to an illegal alien is going to do a drive-by at his local Home Depot store with an AK-47 and try taking out as many illegals as he can.

The timing of the contest couldn't have come at a better time for me, either, because I just completed two paintings in the art class I'm taking.

I can't paint worth a damn—if I were to paint someone's portrait, I'd make Picasso's cubist paintings look realistic by comparison. I figure I still have an outside chance of at least getting second place, because I'm counting on two factors:

#1 That the other paintings by the non–art majors will be crappier than mine.

And

#2 Mexican genetics: the *Mañana Gene* (the Tomorrow Gene).

This gene prevents Mexicans from turning anything in on time. It's an issue that even years of therapy can't fix, because it's a *genetic problem*, not a psychological problem.

11

The Mañana Gene has cost Mexican-American college students literally millions and millions of dollars in financial aid, because most of us are incapable of turning in our financial aid packets on time.

And the Mexicans lucky enough to have turned in their packets on the last day usually don't get any money, anyway. They qualified, but the grant money is all gone by the time their applications are processed because of the chinos - a.k.a., the Asian students.

The chinos always have their financial aid packets filled out and ready to be mailed in a month before the applications are even accepted—I think it's in the chinos' genetic make-up. Well, except for the Filipinos, because the Spaniards conquered them a long time ago, just like Mexico - thus acquiring the debilitating Mañana Gene.

I don't feel bad about calling them chinos. I don't mean anything by it, other than referring to the fact that they are chinos. Chinos means Chinese, and what Mexicans do is what all races do: We lump many groups of similar-looking people into one large group.

For example, Mexicans lump Chinese, Vietnamese, Japanese, Cambodians, Koreans, and every other Asian group together and call them chinos. Even though they're obviously not all Chinese, they get lumped together, anyway.

"I feel like *chino* food," so we go to a Japanese restaurant for some sushi.

"My uncle is a *chino* war veteran," referring to the Vietnam War.

"*Chinos* make good television sets," referring to Samsungs, manufactured in Korea.

The chinos, or Asians, do the same thing to us. We see the chinos as one big lump of *masa* (dough), and they see us as one big lump of *masa* as well. It doesn't matter if they're referring to a Guatemalan, Colombian, or Puerto Rican—to them we're all "a

12

bunch of Mexicans." However, to the extremely naive people, chino or white, we're "Spanish."

When I entered the study room in the library, I only saw Paul and his friend, Jinsoo. There are usually more people there than just those two idiots. I knew they wouldn't be entering the art contest—Paul Gomez is a philosophy major who'd debate way past the deadline as to what constitutes art. Paul is a real wanna-be-Socrates pain in the ass. He's always stressed out in the study room because he can't smoke there. The funny thing about Paul is that he didn't start smoking until he switched his major from biology to philosophy—I think, he thinks, that smoking makes him look more pensive.

I knew Jinsoo wasn't going to be entering the art contest because he's Korean—and not a happy Korean, either. He always talks slow and whiny, as if he's taking a long crap that won't come out.

"What do you have there?" the chino asked me, pointing at the two paintings I was carrying. That simple question alone took him 13 long-ass seconds to ask.

"Why are you asking such an obvious question? They're paintings, fool," Paul answered.

"Why are you *answering* such an obvious question?" Jinsoo responded, giving Paul a "you're the fool" look. "Paintings, huh? But you are not an art major," he said. "Why would you even bother to attempt to paint anything? It makes no sense whatsoever." 24 seconds.

He was right. I wasn't an art major. Hell, I got ADD, and an art class is the last place I should be. The class spent the whole first week drawing an apple-*a freaking apple!* I wanted to drop the class, but I couldn't find another class to get into. While everyone else was focused on the apple, I'd go to the bathroom, study for another class, talk to anybody who'd listen, and do anything else to keep myself entertained.

It only took me *thirty minutes* to draw my apple, *not a whole damn week*. That's why I'm a Liberal Studies major—this degree has a little bit of everything.

Liberal Studies is the perfect degree for those "interested in pursuing a quality education using a multi-disciplinary approach." At least that's what the college catalog says about the degree.

Reading between the lines, though, it means it's the perfect degree for juniors who've taken a lot classes from many different areas but still haven't declared a major, and better declare one soon if they ever want to graduate from college—*and* for those with ADD.

I've never been officially diagnosed with attention deficit disorder, but like my dad says, you don't need a doctor to tell you you're sick if you got diarrhea. And according to the textbook I used in my psychology class my freshman year in college, I have an "upset stomach" regarding my ability to concentrate.

I constantly start new projects before finishing the ones I've already started. I find it hard to sit still. I'm easily distracted. I daydream a lot. When I walk into a bookstore, I can't decide what section to go to: history, art, literature, sociology, or the movie section?

I usually wander around the bookstore for a while until something grabs my attention—kind of like a moth flying around in the dark until it sees a light bulb—except I see all kinds of light bulbs, more like strobe lights going off in front of my eyes, and I don't know which one to go to. Then, after about 10 minutes of being in one section, I get the feeling I'll find something more interesting somewhere else in the bookstore, so I go in search *of that something*.

"I'm entering an art contest to try and win some money,"
I told Jinsoo.

"Maybe I should enter, because those paintings don't look very good," Jinsoo said, pointing to my paintings as I leaned

14

them up against the wall. "Can you give me the information on the contest, because I have a painting at home I did last semester of a sunset that's much better than both of those *combined*. My God, you must have a horrible art professor instructing you. Is it Dr. Cummings?"

"You don't qualify for the contest—you gotta be Mexican-American," I replied.

"What percentage does one have to be Mexican?" Jinsoo asked, "because rumor has it that my family has some Mexican blood, going back about six generations—something about a Mexican cook from an American aircraft carrier and a rebellious great-great-great-great grandmother that had a Latin lover."

Pinche chino now thinks he's a Chicano, I thought to myself.

"So let me get this straight—your real name is Jinsoo Lee Kim Sanchez Jimenez?" Paul asked.

"Forget you, now I'm not going to tell you about our family's shameful past," Jinsoo said, frustrated.

I did notice at a party last year that he dances cumbias pretty good—maybe there is some truth as to what happened six generations ago? I got jealous, I must admit—not only does Jinsoo get his financial aid packets in on time, but he dances cumbias better than me, too.

"So, which painting are you entering in the contest?" Paul asked me.

This was the thousand-dollar question. The two paintings are very different from each other. One painting is titled *Flying Blue Tacos,* and the other one *Self.* I could only enter one, so I have to make sure I pick the one that'll give me the best chance of winning. They both have their pros and cons.

If Dr. Padilla and the selection committee are "Old-School Chicanos," I'll definitely turn in *Flying Blue Tacos.* The painting has blue tacos flying all over the canvas.

15

This painting, with its tacos and bright colors, fulfills the stereotype, or expectations, of what comes to mind when thinking about "Mexican-American art."

There're a handful of themes that many Mexican-American artist feel obligated to paint about: Cesar Chavez, the Virgin de Guadalupe, skeletons, immigrant workers, pachucos, lucha libre wrestlers and quinceañeras, among a dozen other themes. My *Blue Tacos* painting works well within this formula.

This painting also has a direct link with the theme of the contest, because it could be argued that "the taco" is the essence of "Our Community." Throughout the country Mexicans are killing Mexicans—the homeboys from the Southwest 13 gang kill a few homeboys from the Northeast 13 gang, then the Northeast vatos (homeboys) retaliate by killing some Southwest cholos.

On and on this vicious cycle of violence continues, but at the end of the day, what do the gang members do? They go home and eat *tacos*!

Two bitter enemies in the streets, as it turns out, have a passion and a love for the same object. Not blue tacos, I'm sure, unless the cholo's mom shops at Trader Joe's, but tacos nonetheless. If a taco doesn't unite the Mexican-American community, then I don't know what does. At least this is the way I'm hoping Dr. Padilla and the committee see it.

However, if Dr. Padilla and the committee are "New Generation" Mexican-Americans, they may be tired of the "typical Mexican-American themes" and be more interested in my other painting, *Self*.

The *Self* painting looks like I picked up a bunch of brushes with different colors and pushed them all over the canvas with no direction in mind—it looks this way because that's exactly what I did.

I had no idea of what to paint for my second painting in class, especially since my artistic abilities limited my options as to what I could paint, but I had to turn in something on Monday

16

morning. So on Sunday night, out of desperation, I dipped the brushes in the paint and pushed them all around the canvas with no direction in mind. Ten minutes later, I was done. There were green, red, orange, yellow, brown, and many other colors going all over the canvas—it looked like an aerial view of a bunch of freeways intersecting.

Freeways would've been a better title for the painting, but I named it *Self*. Why? I have no idea, but I'm hoping the committee interprets the painting as an existential one. Maybe they'll even say to themselves, "Finally, something other than a Day of the Dead skeleton or an illegal alien working in a strawberry field."

I'm hoping they'll interpret the different lines as different individuals pursuing their own personal goals, but at the same time, at the end of the day, coming together to form a community, a whole, just like Mexican-Americans do every single day of the year throughout cities all over the United States—by pursuing our own dreams and interests, we create a community.

This is what I love about art—some crazy interpretation can be made up, and who's to say that that particular interpretation is wrong? If beauty is in the eye of the beholder, then interpretations are in the mind of the interpreter. I always do pretty good in classes that are open to "interpretation"—a.k.a., bullshit.

Which reminds me of a poem I wrote in tenth grade, after getting my math test back, a subject open to zero interpretation:

To My Math Teacher

I got my grade back

my grade is a D

is this a reflection on

you or me?

17

Personally, I don't favor one painting over the other—I just want to ensure my chances of winning the contest. Dr. Padilla is new to the university, and I've never had him for a class. Hell, I'd never even heard of Dr. Padilla until this contest came around. And since the deadline to apply is two days away, I figure I have enough time to do some research on Dr. Padilla to figure out if he's "Old-School Chicano" or "New-School Mexican-American" before deciding on which painting to turn in.

I worked on the application for about five minutes in the study room before having a sudden urge for some nachos. I wasn't really hungry, but for some reason the thought of hot melted cheese just sounded good—with a Coke and lots of ice.

I got up and left the room without saying anything to Paul or Jinsoo. I hate saying goodbye to people, because I feel it gives them a sense of authority over me—as if I need their approval to leave. I like to just get up and go, as if saying, "Screw you—I don't need to tell you why I'm leaving or where I'm going. You don't control me."

It sounds stupid, but that's what I do. I think it's stupid to eat white rice mixed with ketchup, but that's what my cousin Erica does. We all do stupid things.

While I was standing in the long line, I remembered that I had to take my dad to the bus station. Since I wasn't really hungry, I left the line and started my long walk back to the car so I could give my dad the ride he had asked for yesterday.

My dad wants a ride to the bus station because he's going to Tijuana to have some dental work taken care of. He has insurance through my mother's work, but he always insists on going all the way down to TJ for his dental care.

My mother works at La Habra Community Hospital as a cook's assistant, and even though she makes a bit more than minimum wage, the great thing about her job is that it provides health benefits—including dental. So even though my father could get his dental work taken care of three streetlights away

18

from our house, he insists on traveling over a hundred miles for the same service.

Knowing my dad, he probably goes to the dentist in Tijuana because he gets a free hubcap with every visit, and a sofa reupholstered after ten visits. Something like this has to be the reason for going to TJ for his dental work, because otherwise my dad's actions just don't make any sense.

As I walked towards the car, I was excited about the contest, but I also felt somewhat stupid thinking that I was counting on ugly-ass paintings and lazy Mexicans who don't meet deadlines to win the contest. Hell, I pretty much fall into both of these categories, I realized.

My paintings were done—there wasn't anything I could do about them, now. I just had to focus in on getting the application turned in—chino style, of course.

MEXICAN ENGINEERING

It took me forever to get to my car because I couldn't find parking close to the university in the morning.

I never park in the university's parking lot because they charge way too much for parking permits. I always park in the street, where it's free.

Besides, I wasn't in any hurry to get to my car—it was hot and my car doesn't have air conditioning. And to make matters worse, only the back windows roll down—the two front windows are permanently sealed shut, like a coffin, thanks to my dad.

A few months ago, I told him that the driver's side window was stuck and wouldn't go up all the way. He told me he'd take care of it. He took the paneling off the door, pulled the window all the way up, and secured it in place by wrapping the window rack and the door frame together with wire hangers—that window was never going to budge again! He did the same thing to the passenger's-side window, even though that side wasn't broken.

Now, I know some religions don't believe in certain things— like Jews won't eat pork because the body is a temple, I get that. Mormons don't drink caffeine because, well, I'm not sure why they don't, but I know they don't.

And Mexican fathers *will never*, as if it were part of their religion, take a car to a licensed mechanic or call a licensed contractor to fix anything in the house because they live by the following three Compadre Commandments:

#1 Thou shall try to fix the problem by thyself, after all, what does thou have to lose?

#2 If thou can't fix the problem, call a compadre who can fix the problem.

#3 If thy compadre can't fix the problem, ask thy compadre if he knows of another compadre who can fix the problem, and keep asking around until a capable compadre is located.

It seems like older Mexican fathers believe in a conspiracy theory that "The System" is out to get them—that things break so that those with State Certified Licenses can fix the problems and make lots of money by overcharging customers.

To protect themselves from "The System," a unique branch of engineering has been developed among these cheap cautious men: *Mexican Engineering*.

Mexican Engineering doesn't require classes in linear algebra, differential calculus, or aerodynamics—it just requires a creative mind and a deep-down desire not to pay anyone to fix the problem at hand.

The Mexican Engineering Pledge, also known as The Macho Man Pledge, is designed to complement the three Compadre Commandments:

> *I, el mas chignon (the biggest badass), can fix any problem related to the house or cars using tools and crap I already own or can borrow— therefore, I don't have to go to Home Depot or Jack's Auto Shop to buy the proper tools or materials I really need to fix the pinche problem.*

My father is a strong practitioner of this pledge, with the consequences resulting in him having to take the bus to Tijuana.

The hood on my father's car wouldn't stay shut—whenever he'd hit a bump, the hood would pop open. Instead of having the car checked out and fixed properly, or at least referring to the second *Compadre Commandment*, he used wire hangers to keep the hood from popping open—he wrapped the hangers through the car's grill and the hood to keep it shut.

22

It worked, for a while. But one day he got on the freeway, and the hangers weren't strong enough keep the hood closed—as soon as he hit 70 miles per hour, the hood flew up, smashed the front window, and sent him swerving all over the freeway. He didn't hit any other cars, but the car was no longer drivable—that's why he was taking the bus to TJ.

He still talks to his compadres about how if he only would've just used "two more pinche hangers" to secure the hood, the accident never would've happened.

My father thinks that wire hangers can fix anything—he loves their versatility and strength. He uses them for all of the practical purposes everyone else in the neighborhood uses them for: to hang bird cages from the porch; as car antennas; to secure a piñata on a rope; to scrape junk out between the car seats; to keep a muffler from scraping on the ground.

My dad uses hangers so much, some people now call him *Gancho Man (Hanger Man)*.

HONDA CHOLOS

Once I got in my car, I rolled down the two rear windows and took off.

Ten minutes later, I was going west on Imperial Highway in La Habra. While at a red light, a car full of cholos pulled up next to me. I thought for sure that my worst nightmare was finally going to take place: I was going to be killed by a cholo.

They weren't "friendly" looking cholos, either. Friendly cholos drive around in beautiful low-riders with expensive paint jobs and kick-ass stereo systems. Many will have a mural of the Virgin de Guadalupe, skulls, or a seductive chola painted on the hood—or sometimes they'll have all three painted throughout the car. Cholos in nice cars aren't looking for trouble—they don't wanna mess up their ride.

The cholos that society needs to keep an eye out for are the ones who drive around in 1989, dented-up silver Honda Accords with Señor Frog's license plate frames and that are missing two hubcaps. These are the vatos that have nothing to lose.

And suddenly there they were next to me with their windows rolled down—apparently they don't have air conditioning, either.

My nightmare isn't so much about just being killed by a cholo—it's being mistaken for a white guy by a cholo, *and then being killed by him.* I don't want to be shot in the head by a cholo, and then have him say to his homeboys, after hearing on the evening news that a guy named "Hector Zamora" was his victim, "Damn, I thought he was a white dude, not Mexican! *Dispensa.*" (My bad)

The nightmare I keep imagining will be played out after pulling up to a red light—my windows will be up, and I'll be singing along with Vicente Fernandez on the radio. I'll be singing 'Amor de la Calle' out loud, when the Honda cholos will pull up next to me.

From the cholo's point of view, in the Accord, he'll look over and see what he thinks is a white guy singing along to a Willie Nelson song.

I'll really be singing-

"Amor de la calle, que vendes tus besos a cambio de amor..."

but in his mind he hears me singing-

"On the road again, I just can't wait to get on the road again, the life I love is makin' music with my friends, and I just can't wait to get on the road again..."

The cholo will then think to himself, "I hate white people and their dumb-ass country music. It's time I kill one of them." And he does! He pulls out his 357 and shoots me in the head.

I imagine the cholo being a high-school dropout who has never heard of the Chicano Moratorium or Lopez Tijerina. But he pulls out his gun and kills the guy who was going to be a teacher—the teacher who would've taught his children that more than 30,000 Mexican-Americans marched in the Chicano Moratorium in 1970 because a disproportionate number of patriotic soldiers with surnames like Gomez, Sanchez, Gutierrez, and Suarez were dying in the Vietnam War, and that the march ended with the murder of a reporter, resulting in the birth of an icon: Ruben Salazar.

I also would've taught his kids about Corky Gonzales' epic poem: I Am Joaquin. But since their father killed me 15 years earlier, they ended up being taught by an apathetic teacher who was only working in the low-income, predominantly Mexican school so that the government would pay off his student loans— and instead of "refusing to be absorbed," as stated in the poem, the cholitos end up being completely absorbed into the mainstream's culture, void of any knowledge of their past or present Mexican heritage.

That's how I imagine my nightmare playing out.

However, I'm not going down without a fight—I have some proactive maneuvers designed to keep me alive. For years I've been anticipating the day a cholo in a bad mood pulls up next to me.

"Plan A" involves me playing a *Tigres del Norte* CD and turning up the volume really loud so they'll know I'm *puro Mexicano*! (pure Mexican!) I've even considered throwing in a grito (shout of joy), but since they'll think I'm a white guy, they may interpret my grito as a condescending gesture and decide to beat the crap out of me instead of shooting me—and if I'm going to die, I want to die quickly and with the least amount of pain.

"Plan B" involves me pretending I'm talking on the phone to my mother in Spanish. I'll talk really loud so the cholos will be able to hear me—"¿*Dónde está mi lápiz? (Where's my pencil?) Tengo hambre! (I'm hungry!) Me duele la cabeza! (I have a headache!)*"

The plan is to keep talking long enough to confuse them, and then when the light turns green I'll take off quicker than a fly that's about to be swatted by a chino with a black belt in karate.

But both of these plans are predicated on my ability to roll down my window at the red light so they'll be able to hear the Mexican music or me talking out loud in Spanish. These plans are no longer viable options thanks to my father—little did he know that when he permanently shut my front windows, he also put my life in mortal danger.

This is why I had to come up with a "Plan C." I put a huge sticker of one of Mexico's most popular soccer teams on my bumper—the Chivas de Guadalajara. If this doesn't say "wetback on board," I don't know what does.

The only thing that could go wrong with this plan is if a cholo whose favorite team is Club America from Mexico City pulls up next to me, because the Chivas and Club America fans detest each other more than the Koreans and the Japanese detest each other.

27

My heart started pumping really fast when I saw the cholo in the back seat of the car reaching down, as if to grab a gun. I slammed my eyes shut, anticipating the bullets that'd soon be entering the side of my skull, wondering to myself, "Didn't he see my Chivas bumper sticker?"

But the only sound I heard was the car behind me honking — the cholos had already taken off. As I drove off, I thought of a new poem:

The cholos pulled up

next to me, but

nothing happened

I continued down Imperial Highway and made a right turn on Walnut Street. I was going to stop off at the 7-11 on the corner, but I realized that I had forgotten my wallet at home, which meant it was a good thing I got out of the nachos line at school, since I wouldn't have been able to pay for the food.

I made a left turn on Las Lomas and headed home to the Las Lomas Garden Apartment Complex — even though there aren't any gardens there. The apartment complex itself is pretty big — it has more than 200 units.

APARTMENT A-7

The Las Lomas apartments are government-funded, low-income units.

We moved into them when they were first built. They're pretty nice apartments—considering they were built for poor families. Fortunately, or unfortunately, I should say, we qualified to live there.

Although the overall quality of the apartments is good, there is a problem that most of the residents complain about—the walls between the units are too thin.

The thin walls weren't really an issue with us—that is, until Ms. Abazy moved in next door with her four kids from three different men. She had *government funding* written all over her. The kids were constantly fighting and throwing things at one another. Ms. Abazy had a voice louder than a lion's, and even when she was being nice it sounded like she was roaring at her kids.

I loved growing up in the apartment complex, though. Since they are government funded, I always had a bunch of kids to play with—it was like always being at a Chuck E. Cheese's on a Saturday afternoon. Well, a poor man's Chuck E. Cheese's, more like a *Pedro y Queso (Pedro and Cheese)*.

Parents in the complex didn't have to hire a baby-sitter whenever they'd go to a wedding, movie, or a family function. They'd just toss the children outside and have them run around with the other kids all day and into the night—parents knew that somehow, somewhere, their kids would be fed by someone.

We still live in apartment A-7, just as most of the kids I grew up with still live in their apartments. Tim and Terry live in A-10. Oscar Ibarra lives in A-11. Steve Cruz lives in A-2. Olivia Zeta lives next door—and these are only the kids who lived in the "A" building.

When we were kids, we played in the back of the apartment complex all day and night, rain or shine. There were dozens and dozens of other kids running around the back of the complex as well. It seemed that whenever a family moved out, two more moved in—there was never a dull moment.

We'd race blades of grass or small branches down the street gutter whenever it'd rain—or when we'd "accidently" break a water sprinkler. We climbed every tree in the complex. We'd ding-dong-ditch every apartment at least once a month. We played football, soccer, and baseball in the carport alley. Every evening there'd be more than twenty kids on their bikes racing around the entire complex to see who was the fastest.

The hide-and-seek games were legendary. Tom Rice always won because he was the only one able to climb up the long skinny tree so he could hide on the carport roof. However, after he fell from the roof and broke his leg in three different places, he never won again. Even 5-year-old kids were now able to make him "It" in tag. He was easy to hit in dodge ball, too. Nobody wanted Tom on their team anymore because he walked slow and crooked. The only person who'd pick him was Otis, *The Black Superman.*

Mexicans and whites made up most of the families living in the apartment complex. There was only one black person in the whole place, Otis, and we all looked up to him.

We called him *The Black Superman* because he once hit a record 16 shots in a row during a basketball game. He was a great basketball player—for a 40-year-old alcoholic on Disability playing mostly against 10-year-old kids.

Otis was everyone's counselor, too. Any time, any day, Otis was always there for us, giving us advice on everything from dealing with our parents to how to meet girls. Everyone was sad the day he moved away, but we got over him pretty fast, thanks to our "discovery" in the Dumpster.

One day, while looking for the baseball that Dean had hit into a trash bin, we found some Victoria's Secret catalogs.

After finding that stuff, we went Dumpster diving all the time in search of more "treasures." There were more than ten big trash bins throughout the complex, so we were pretty busy. We must've recorded 40 Dumpster-diving hours within the first week of finding those catalogs. If they had been scuba diving hours, we probably would've gotten a Certificate of Completion for Scuba Diving or something. We didn't play basketball or baseball for a while after finding that stuff.

Dumpster diving wasn't anything new to me—my father had us doing it all the time. Unfortunately for us, my father found a very nice watch in one of the Dumpsters the first week we moved into the apartments. After that, he had us jumping in the trash bins all over the apartment complex to see what we'd find. At the very least, he wanted us to return with a plastic shopping bag full of aluminum cans.

However, in all of our years of Dumpster diving, we never found anything good—after all, what could we find rummaging through poor people's trash?

After the watch, the next best thing we ever found was a hair dryer that was still in the box. It doesn't sound like much, but the image of my mother jumping up and down after my brother handed her the box is still fresh in my mind.

One of the best parts about growing up in the complex was Halloween. Since the apartments were close to each other, it was easy to collect large amounts of candy in a short period of time. My record was three-and-a-half pillowcases full of candy. It would've been four pillowcases of candy, but my father always had dibs on the first stash of candy we'd collect—he refused to buy candy to pass out to the trick-or-treaters. Instead, he'd send us, my two brothers and sister and me out early to collect candy.

After we'd get about half a pillowcase worth of candy, we'd go home and give it to my dad—this was the candy he'd pass out

31

to the kids knocking on our door. After that, though, the rest of the candy was ours—and I had the cavities to prove it.

But for the very good stuff, we had to travel to the other side of Whittier Boulevard—to the North Hills neighborhood between Harbor Boulevard and Palm Avenue. My father would cram the car with as many kids as possible and head on up to the houses where some of the apartment complex kids' parents worked as maids and gardeners. My mother ironed the clothes for Mrs. Lockwood to earn extra money—she lived in a big blue house on Pine Edge Drive.

In our apartment complex, we'd always get, without fail, some weird "treats" passed out to us.

~ The religious freak in B-6 always passed out pictures of Jesus.

~ Mrs. Cisneros, for some reason, would pass out a handful of sunflower seeds—not a packet of sunflower seeds, *but a handful.*

~ Mr. Walker always handed out the crayons and coloring books his grandchildren would leave behind when they'd visit him.

~ The skinny lady from apartment C-8 always passed out apples and oranges. I guess she was hoping her healthy habits would rub off on us.

~ And one time, someone gave me packets of sugar!

Most of the stuff we got was okay, but I think some people saw Halloween as an opportunity to empty their cabinets of all the crap they didn't want anymore.

On the other hand, the rich people that lived in North Hills always passed out good stuff—entire Snickers, Milky Ways, and Babe Ruth bars—not the tiny ones. Big Skittle bags and big boxes of Cracker Jacks were also passed out.

My favorite houses were the ones that'd leave the buckets of candy out on the porch with some dumb sign saying, "Take only *one* piece of candy, please." *Yeah, right.* If these people knew that I had just been given a handful of sunflower seeds and five packets of sugar, I think they'd understand why I'd always take three handfuls of their candy—we always made a killing with their honor system.

The people that did answer their doors were very nice. I guess they all knew one another, because the person passing out the candy would often try and guess who the trick-or-treaters were. They'd say things like, "Is that you, Billy? Is that you, Jennifer?" - and we'd just nod our heads in the affirmative.

Once in a while, someone would screw up and answer, "*Sí*, it's *yo—Yenifer*." But for the most part, they had no idea they were handing out candy to *Hectors, Pablos, Marias,* and *Consuelos*-and not to Billys, Toms, Pattys, and Jennifers.

Nevertheless, if I had a choice between growing up in the Las Lomas Garden Apartments, or growing up in the North Hills neighborhood - I'd definitely pick the apartments.

Sure, the firemen brought us presents for Christmas, but I just thought it was cool at the time, not that it was because we were poor.

Sure, we had 20 pounds of free government cheese in the fridge, but so did everyone else in the complex.

Sure, I shared a bedroom with my two brothers and wore their hand-me-down clothes, but I always had a lot of clothes to choose from.

But did I have a happy childhood growing up in the apartment complex? I sure did.

I parked the car along the street gutter from where we used to race the blades of grass on rainy days and went inside the apartment to get my father. He wasn't there, but my oldest brother, Santiago, was.

"Where's my dad?" I asked Santiago.

33

"I don't know. I just got here, too. Go ask my mom where he's at," Santiago responded.

"She's at work, you *idiot*. I was supposed to take my dad to the bus station," I said, frustrated.

"Don't get mad at me, *stupid*. You know how my dad is—he probably found someone going to TJ today and went with them." Santiago was right—my dad would sit on someone's bumper all the way to TJ to save a buck. I was on my way upstairs to get my wallet from my bedroom when my sister walked in.

"Do you know where my dad is?" I asked Sophia. She looked mad.

"*You* should know where he is, *stupid*—you were supposed to have taken him to the bus station, not me. Now I'm going to be late for work!" Sophia grunted as she stomped her way past me on the stairs heading to her room. "You're taking my mom to work tomorrow!" she yelled out before slamming her bedroom door. My "punishment" had been handed down.

My mother works in the hospital's kitchen, and her shift starts at 5:30 in the morning. And thanks to my father's desire to keep control over his wife, she never learned how to drive. Either he didn't want her to have any independence, or he was too cheap to buy her a car. Whichever reason it was, most likely both, we all take turns driving her to work in the mornings. My dad would give her a ride to work, but he himself goes into work at 4:00 in the morning.

I feel bad for my mom. Every morning she hears us fighting about who's going to give her a ride to work.

"You take her, *stupid*, I have a test in the morning!"

"You take her, *idiot*, I couldn't sleep all night!"

"You take her, *fool*, I have a headache!"

"You take her, *ass*, I had my license revoked!"

Eventually, some *stupid-ass-idiot* would take her—license or not.

I don't know what it is about my brothers and sister, but we call each other a lot of names. Stupid-idiot-fool-ass-pendejo. These are the main names we use.

I honestly don't know where this name-calling stems from, because we do love one another. We get along. We can count on one another. I'll call my sister a name, and 2 seconds later she'll loan me 10 bucks. My brother will call me an idiot, then I'll lend him my car. We don't hold grudges against one another for more than 5 seconds. Well, maybe a couple of hours. Talking harshly towards one another is just part of our language, unfortunately.

The other thing we do is say "*my* dad" and "*my* mom," even though we all have the same parents. Our neighbors and cousins always make fun of us for talking that way.

Maybe we all have some deep-down unresolved childhood issues we haven't discovered yet? At least we say "*my* dad" instead of "*your* dad." This has to have some positive meaning to Freudians.

With my wallet in hand and my father no longer needing a ride to the bus station, I headed back to school. This time I'm going down Lambert Street—to avoid the Honda cholos I had seen earlier on Imperial Hwy.

MOVIE-MEN-TOE

I finally found a parking spot and headed towards the library.

As the elevator doors opened up, I saw Fred Suarez, the Emperor, exiting the elevator.

"See you at the meeting," he said as he walked past me in a rush.

I had forgotten about the LBSA meeting. LBSA stands for Latino Business Student Association. I was the farthest thing from a Business Major. Macro and microeconomics seemed as interesting to study as, well, macro and microeconomics — but I was in the club anyway.

After graduating from La Habra High School, I did what my older brother and sister did: I attended Fullerton College. It used to be called Fullerton *Junior* College, but it wanted to sound more respectable, so it changed its name to Fullerton *Community* College. After several years the term "Community" was looked down on, so the school got rid of "Community" in the title and now goes by the simpler, more respectable name: Fullerton College. At least that's the story I remember my literature instructor telling us.

Attending a community college seemed like the natural progression for me. I never talked to a counselor about going to a four-year university, nor did any teacher or counselor ever encourage me to apply to a university.

I don't blame them for not encouraging me. I never gave them a reason to seek me out — I was a 2.65 GPA student, and that's counting all of the As in my PE classes. Personally, I don't think that's too bad of a GPA considering I never did any

37

homework or studied for tests. My 2.65 GPA was nothing but raw, God-given intelligence.

Going to college was something I always knew I was going to do—there was never any doubt about it. It never occurred to me, however, to look into a university. Maybe it was because I had a good grip on reality. With my GPA, I didn't have a chance of getting accepted anywhere. I filled out one application for college, and they had to accept me—community colleges have to accept everybody.

Many people enter the community college system, but only a few of us make it out. Community colleges are like tar pits—lots of dinosaurs got trapped in the tar pits and died. Only the strong dinosaurs were able to free themselves and continue on their journey, just as only the strong-minded students are able to escape the suction of the community colleges and transfer to four-year universities.

By the time it came to transferring out of Fullerton College, the vast majority of the people I knew from high school had already dropped out. A few transferred to other community colleges because they specialized in certain areas. Cerritos College, or maybe it's Cypress College, has a good nursing program, while Rio Hondo College has a strong police and fire academy.

In the end, only one person I knew ended up transferring to Cal State Fullerton: Nick. But we hardly ever see each other because the campus is so big. My first year there, I didn't meet anyone new.

It's not that I'm antisocial or anything, it's just that even though the campus is crawling with tons of students, most of them are like me: either crawling to class or crawling home. That's pretty much what happens at commuter schools—unless, of course, you join a club. So that's what I decided to do—I joined a club because I was tired of feeling like an island unto myself.

At Cal State Fullerton each semester starts off with the clubs setting up booths in the quad in the hopes of recruiting new students, like me. I saw the booths being set up last fall and spring semesters, but I didn't pay any attention to them at the time. However, after a year of "solitary confinement" at the university, I was now willing to join some of the "inmates." The first day I saw the booths set up, I decided to check them out.

It felt kind of weird for me walking around the booths. It reminded me of when I go to nightclubs and walk around looking for just the right girl to ask to dance—I'm nervous because the possibility of rejection is everywhere.

After 10 minutes into my journey, none of the clubs caught my attention. There was the Ski Club. This Mexican don't ski. There was a Chess Club, but I don't even like to play checkers. And there was no way I'd ever join the Chemistry or Astronomy Clubs—I got a D in both of those subjects, including extra credit.

Then I saw someone I recognized: Ramon. He's the president of MEChA. Ramon was standing in front of MEChA's table with another student, most likely the vice-president of the club.

I gave him a "what's up" with my chin, but he didn't respond. I don't know if he ignored me because he didn't see me, doesn't like me, or is still pissed off at me about the recommendations I had made in the class we had taken together.

It was a sociology class, and the assignment was to evaluate a club from the university and make recommendations on how the club could be improved by appealing to a broader base of students.

I was assigned MEChA, Ramon's club. At the end of the semester, after researching the club, I presented to the class the following recommendations.

Recommendation #1—Change the club's name

MEChA stands for Movimiento Estudiantil Chicano de Aztlan. In English this means "Chicano Student Movement from Aztlan." It might have been a good name for the club back in the '60s and '70s, but today it's about as appealing to young Mexican-American students as, well, MEChA.

The fact that Cal State Fullerton has more than 8,000 Mexican-American students, but only 12 of them are MEChA members, well-this clearly demonstrates its lack of appeal.

I recommended changing the name, first of all, because the name is in Spanish. This might intimidate students who want to join the club but don't speak Spanish.

For example, what if a proud-ass Chicano, say his name is "Mario," with the Aztec God Tonatiuh tattooed on his chest, as proof of his *Brown and Proud* pride, wants to join the club but doesn't speak Spanish? What if he told a friend that he wants to join MEChA, and the friend asks him, "What does MEChA stand for?" Mario would sound stupid, saying-

"Movie-Men-Toe, East-to-do-and-till, Chick-can-0, Day, Ass-tlan."

Who'd ever take him seriously pronouncing the name like that? He'd be better off joining the Chess Club.

I'm sure there are some Mario-type members who've quit the club because they couldn't pronounce the name, but I bet there's a hell of a lot more *who never joined in the first place*, for the same reason.

I myself hate speaking Spanish to my true-blue wetback friends and cousins because they always make fun of my pocho-Spanish. From what I've observed, this goes on within MEChA as well.

I'd also change the name because most members don't even know what Aztlan is. I passed out a blank sheet of paper to several MEChA members and asked them to write down what Aztlan referred to.

Several got it right, but most didn't. One member wrote that Aztlan is in Texas and is the location where the Mexican army defeated the American army. *"Remember the Aztlan!"* is what some fool wrote down.

How can the club say they're a student movement from Aztlan, when many of the students don't even know what Aztlan is?

I ended this section by stating that MEChA can either continue having only a handful of members by keeping its name, or take a chance by reinventing itself and possibly increasing its membership.

Recommendation #2—Change the logo

MEChA's logo is that of an eagle, a somewhat Nazi-looking eagle holding a stick of dynamite with a lit fuse in one talon and an Aztec weapon in the other.

It looks like the eagle is pissed off and is about to commit either suicide or a terrorist attack—it's not a very welcoming logo.

I suggested that each club adapt a logo that appeals to its particular region. An obvious example would be the Alamo for MEChA Clubs around San Antonio - or for all of Texas, for that matter.

Instead of having a bipolar eagle, they should have the Alamo as their logo instead. The Mexican Army killed a bunch of white guys after attacking the Alamo—it goes perfect with their philosophy, which states, "vow to work for the liberation of Aztlan."

If what took place at the Alamo doesn't symbolize *working for the liberation of Aztlan*, then I don't know what does.

Changing logos isn't anything new—companies do it all the time to become more recognizable, to appeal to a larger market. Pepsi, Starbucks, and even Walmart have all changed their logos throughout the years, and they're doing quite well.

MEChA can't be afraid of making changes. As it stands right now, MEChA is only surviving—changes may help it thrive. When changes aren't made to meet the needs of the many, those few that don't want the changes become the dictators—the oppressors.

All dictators eventually get overthrown. At the university club level, however, the overthrow takes place when the students simply stop showing up to the club's meetings. It's pretty much a bloodless and silent uprising.

Recommendation #3—Make the club academically based

The perception of the club is that it's composed of politically active, disgruntled Chicanos who like to blame "The System" for their problems—MEChA is synonymous with "bitter students with chips on their shoulders."

And MEChA officers aren't just angry at "The System"- they get angry towards anyone with an opposing view within the club as well. I bet if a member stood up at a meeting and said, "We should crack down on illegal aliens because they're taking their toll on the American economy," the club members would all stand up and get ready to beat his ass.

But if he followed that remark up with, "I mean crack down on *chino* illegal aliens!" they'd give him a standing ovation and some sort of honorary award. He may even be promoted to Club President on the spot.

A way to start changing this perception would be to make the club academically based. Set the bar high for the members. What if the officers in the club have to maintain a minimum 3.25 GPA, and the members have to have a 3.0 GPA to be in the club?

This way, when someone says he's a member of MEChA, people will think, "*Wow*, he's an *intelligent* Chicano," instead of, "*Damn*, he must be a *bitter* Chicano."

How cool would it be to say, "I'm a member of MEChA," and that be synonymous with academic success?

Anyway, these were my recommendations and explanations. I guess Ramon and MEChA got the last laugh, though. I got a C on my project because the assignment was to focus in on *realistic changes* that could possibly be implemented at the local level, and, apparently, I was way off the mark.

As I walked up to Ramon's table, he turned around and made it seem as if he was going through a box looking for something. This worked out great for me because I thought I was going to have to converse with him for a few minutes to legitimize taking a pan dulce that was on a tray—I decided to grab three of them since he wasn't looking, and I continued walking among the booths set up all over the place.

I was getting ready to give up the search for a club to join when I noticed a white banner across a table. Printed across the banner were bold, black, and boring letters with the club's name: Latino Business Student Association.

There was a girl and a guy standing behind the table. They were dressed like bankers-or morticians. They looked weird because they were wearing what looked like matching black business suits—either his was too feminine or hers was too masculine. As I approached them, I felt like I should've had a deposit slip in my hand, or the name of a loved one I needed to have buried.

I'm sure they weren't too thrilled to see me walking up to them, either. I was dressed as if I was going to buy donuts on a Saturday morning. I was wearing my Dodgers cap backwards, an old blue shirt that had lost most of its blue color, and pants that were thrashed at the hems from stepping on them all the time.

I knew they were hoping I was just going to ask them where the nearest bathroom was, but I disappointed them by asking instead, "Do you gotta be a business major to join the club?"

The "bank manager" looked at the "head teller" for a quick second. She didn't stare at my clothing, but I knew she had already registered my appearance in her mind.

I was starting to think I should just turn around and walk away because these two fools had as much personality as mannequins.

"No, you don't," she finally responded in a low, monotone voice.

Then they both just looked at me, waiting for me to make the next move. They didn't introduce themselves like businesspeople would've introduced themselves to a potential new client. Nor did they hand me the flyer that was on the table containing information about the club.

If this had been the real business word, I would've fired their asses for poor customer service and taken my business elsewhere. But since this was school and not the real world, and especially since I didn't have anywhere else to take my ass, I put down my pan dulces, reached out my hand, and introduced myself.

Later that week, I attended my first LBSA meeting. I signed in on the sheet being passed around, and just like that I was in the club. I didn't get jumped in; I didn't have to pass a test or make a donation. It was a "no-cut" club—they took everyone, just like community colleges and high school football teams. I didn't even own a tie, and yet I was in a business club? Talk about low standards.

When I finally showed up to the LBSA meeting, Fred, known as The Emperor, was running the meeting because the president and vice-president of the club were at a conference in Anaheim. Everybody likes The Emperor. He knows that we call him The Emperor, but he doesn't really know the reason why. He thinks we call him The Emperor because he's a "take-charge" type of guy—a great leader. And he is. However, the real reason we called him The Emperor is because he's as short as an Emperor penguin.

The Emperor loves being involved in clubs—he had been ASB president of his high school and of his community college back in Sacramento. Currently, he's a school Senator and LBSA's Treasurer.

If he were only 5 inches taller, his political career would be limitless in the real world. Unfortunately for him, voters prefer tall politicians. Short politicians have a reputation of sitting in dark corner booths, smoking cigars, and sipping chicken soup while taking union bribes.

44

Not surprisingly, a lot of members in the club have nicknames. Pepe is called *La Ambulancia,* The Ambulance, because he'll pick up any type of girl: short, tall, fat, skinny, ugly, and ugly as hell, to name a few.

Oscar is called *El Tomate,* The Tomato, because when he gets mad or embarrassed, he turns red—and his cheeks are as fat as a tomato. His mother gave him this nickname when he was 3 years old.

Erika was called *Madonna,* because one night she got drunk at a party that had a karaoke machine and kept singing "Like a Virgin" over and over. Later, after we found out she had a 2-year-old son, someone who had obviously taken an art class changed her nickname to *Madonna with Child*, as in the painting by Raphael.

The Emperor was talking about available internships, upcoming conferences, and other stuff I never pay attention to. Most of the members, being business majors, were taking notes on the information being given—I couldn't care less.

As a matter of fact, my main motivation for showing up at the meeting was to run into Lourdes, not to network.

Lourdes is beautiful and nice. Those two adjectives usually don't go together—it's usually one or the other. Lourdes has a spot of green on her right eye. It looks cool. I'm always asking her, "Do you still have the green spot on your eye?"

I'm not very good with the ladies. I guess that's why I keep asking her the same question. I'm so bad with the ladies, that last week I was rejected by a 400-pound girl sitting on a reinforced barstool. I think it had more to do with my pick-up line rather than my looks—at least that's what I'd like to think.

A great song came on at the club and I wanted to dance— hell, who doesn't feel like dancing to *Atomic Dog?* I saw the big girl sitting alone, tapping her toes, so I figured she'd want to dance, too. I went up to her and said, "It looks like you should burn a few calories. Would you like to dance?" She just flipped me off and turned around—keeping all of her calories to herself.

I must've asked Lourdes a thousand times if she still had the green spot on her eye.

Any other girl by now would've said, "What do you think, fool?" But not Lourdes. The only problem with her, as far as getting together with her, is that she just broke up with her boyfriend—they'd been together since third grade or something like that. It doesn't take a genius to figure out that "rebound guy" seldom, if ever, ends up with the girl. But I still wanted to be around her.

After 10 minutes and no Lourdes in sight, I finally asked Madonna with Child if she'd seen Lourdes around. Madonna with Child told me Lourdes was in a study group, preparing for an exam.

I stood up and walked out of the conference room—no sense in listening to all that business crap if there wasn't a chance of Lourdes showing up. I headed to the Student Center to get the nachos I'd been thinking of all day.

WHAT'S A MAGU?

As I passed the library, I saw two girls I knew sitting on a bench: Blanca and Tina.

Blanca is a member of both LBSA and MEChA. However, since both clubs have their meetings at the same time, one week she'll attend a MEChA meeting, then the next week she'll attend the LBSA meeting.

Blanca says she can't totally commit to either club because she isn't sure which club best meets her "personal needs" — whatever the hell that means. Blanca's plan is to keep attending both clubs, until one of them feels "more right" than the other.

Because she can't commit to one side or the other, someone gave her the nickname of *La Bi,* as in bipolar, I guess.

Blanca was talking to Tina—a devout MEChA member, even though she doesn't speak Spanish. Tina puts a dent in my argument about how students won't join MEChA if they can't pronounce the name—sort of.

Her way of avoiding mispronouncing *Movimiento Estudiantil Chicano de Aztlan* is simple—she never says the club's name in Spanish. Instead, she always gives the English translation—Chicano Student Movement of Aztlan—and then walks away.

Actually, Tina does know some Spanish. She knows three words, to be exact—*órale (right on), chale (hell no),* and *simon (hell yeah).* Because she says these words with a lot of passion, people just assume she knows Spanish.

If Tina gets a test back with a good grade, or wins a free dinner at the Student Center on Tuesday nights, she yells out...

"Órale!"

47

When someone asks her if she had a good time at the party, she yells out...

"Simon! Simon!"

"Chale!" is Tina's favorite response, though.

"Tina, do you want more coffee?"

"Chale!"

"Tina, did you work last night?"

"Chale!"

"Excuse me, young lady; are those your keys on the floor?

"Chale!"

"I'm sorry, what does "*sha-lay*" mean?

"It means, *they ain't my keys*, lady."

Last year, Tina made 150 tamales in one night, by herself, to sell at the Day of the Dead celebration on campus—now that's dedication. All of the money generated went straight to MEChA's scholarship fund. Tina didn't even want to get reimbursed for the stuff she bought to make the tamales.

Rumor has it that she got a tamal de azúcar (sweet tamale) tattooed on the left cheek of her ass to commemorate her accomplishment.

Some people don't understand Mexico's Day of the Dead celebration. I don't think it's that complicated. To celebrate the Day of the Dead, some Mexicans take the dead person's favorite foods and drinks to their gravesite—what's so complicated about that?

"But why would you do that?" I remember one of my white classmates asking me back in high school. "It's not like they can eat the food that's taken to them," he said, while making a gesture with his outstretched arms, as if saying, "what's the point, then?"

It just so happened that his aunt had died earlier in the school year, so I asked him if he had taken his aunt any flowers to her grave since her burial. He said he had.

"Why?" I asked him. "It's not like your aunt is going to punch a hole through her coffin, reach up through 6 feet of dirt, grab the flowers, and then pull them back down into her coffin in appreciation of your gesture—so why even bother taking her the flowers in the first place? They're just going to sit there—*like the food*," I responded while making a "what's the point?" gesture right back at him.

He understood the Day of the Dead celebration after that explanation. As a matter of fact, 2 weeks later he told me that he left a Big Gulp from 7-11 on his aunt's grave—a mixture of Coke and Fruit Punch because that was her favorite drink. His father smacked him on the back of the head, though—his father thought he was being disrespectful by littering on her grave.

To this day, whenever he visits his aunt, he takes her her favorite foods: Doritos, donuts, chicken nuggets, a chocolate shake, and all kinds of other crap is left on her grave. I guess this explains why his aunt was obese, confined to a wheelchair, diabetic, and dead due to heart failure at the age of 45.

I walked up to Blanca and Tina hoping to find out if either of them had ever had Dr. Padilla for a class. As I approached them, Tina got up to go somewhere. I started explaining my dilemma about the art contest to Blanca. A few minutes later, Tina returned.

"What're you guys talking about?" Tina asked.

"Have you ever had Dr. Padilla, the art professor?" Blanca asked Tina. Just then, Paul and Jinsoo walked up with their lunches. They sat down next to Blanca, and Paul offered her some of his sandwich. Paul and Blanca have known each other since the third grade.

"Chale!" Tina responded. "I didn't even know there was a Chicano in the Art Department. Why?"

"Well, that's the thing. Hector wants to know if he's more 'Chicano' or more, say, 'Mexican-American,'" Blanca replied.

"What's the difference between a Chicano and a Mexican-American?" the chino asked.

"*There's a huge difference*," Tina quickly responded, with an unfavorable tone in her voice.

"I don't get it. Chicano, Latino, Spanish, Mexican-American, Puerto Rican, Hispanic—it's all the same, right? You guys speak Spanish, right? Isn't that what bonds you guys together? You guys are all Spanish, right?" Jinsoo continued asking, oblivious to Tina's reaction.

If Tina's eyes were capable of shooting destructive red laser beams, they would've blasted Jinsoo's head and sent his brains flying everywhere. Instead, she was only capable of giving Jinsoo a dirty look—as if she was going to chop him up on the spot and make another 150 tamales out of him.

Jinsoo calmly asked, "What did I say?"

"Chicanos are proud of our culture and history, and we refuse to be marginalized by mainstream society and ignorant fools like your sorry-ass, so *órale!*" Tina responded.

Out of nowhere, Blanca added, "And the parents of Chicanos *have to of been born in Mexico.*"

Blanca was all-proud of herself, as if she had just finished revealing the answer to a difficult question.

Paul smelled blood in the water. "So, anybody whose parents were born in the United States can't be a Chicano?" he asked.

I knew what Paul was up to. Jinsoo knew what Paul was up to. Blanca knew what Paul was up to. Paul was going to demonstrate why people hate philosophy majors.

Before majoring in philosophy, Paul was a biology major. He needed to take a humanities class, so he signed up for Philosophy 101, with Professor Kepler. Turned out, Professor Kepler was a great teacher, and he made philosophy come alive for Paul—so much so that Paul ended up switching majors.

Today, Paul's favorite philosopher is Socrates. Apparently, nobody liked Socrates because he wanted everyone to have definitions for things, because if something can't be defined, it doesn't exists, or some crap like that.

For example: love. If a definition of love can't be applied universally, like the laws of physics, then a new definition of love has to be given. If a universal definition of love can't be given, then, so the argument goes, at least according to Socrates, love doesn't exist.

I think that's how it goes—hell, I got a C- in Philosophy; I could very easily be wrong. Anyway, what Socrates would do is question every definition someone would give for love, and eventually render the definition useless. This pissed off his fellow Athenians. And idiot Paul, in search of an identity, I guess, wanted to be a disciple of Socrates.

Last year he made Blanca cry because he asked her if she loved her boyfriend. She said she did. Paul then asked Blanca for her definition of love.

"Love means I would do anything in the world for that person," Blanca responded.

"Would you rob a bank for your boyfriend?" Paul asked.

"*Stupid!* Of course not."

"Then you don't love your boyfriend. Try a different definition of love."

"I can't help but smile when I think of him. How's that one?"

"Do you love your dad?"

51

"Yeah, of course."

"Do you smile whenever you think of him? Remember, I live three houses over from you. I've seen him beat you guys with a belt for no good reason. I know he's a mean son-of-a-bitch."

"That's a different type of love. He's mean, but I love him."

"The definition you give for love has to be applicable to your boyfriend, your dad, your mother, and anyone else you claim to love. So since you can't define love, you don't know what love is, and therefore you can't love or be loved."

Just then Blanca's boyfriend showed up, so she asked him for his definition of love.

"To me, love means, well, that you love being around someone," her boyfriend responded, smiling at Blanca. She just gave him a mean glare.

"What'd I say?" he asked.

"You love me just like you love *your dog*? Is that all I am to you? *Another dog*?" Blanca asked.

"What're you talking about, Blanca?"

"I know you love to be with your dog—you take that damn thing everywhere! Your definition of love applies to me *and your dog*! That sucks!" Blanca yelled out as she walked away in tears.

Two days later, the boyfriend gave the dog away to his cousin. Three days after that, he got the dog back from his cousin and broke up with Blanca. It's hard to compete against man's best friend, I guess.

"*Oh*, I think at least *one* parent needs to have been born in Mexico—I think," Blanca responded, now somewhat less confident in her knowledge regarding the requirements it takes to be a Chicano.

52

"*Chale*, Blanca, both parents could've been born in the United States—it doesn't matter where the Chicano's parents were born! See, Blanca, this is why you shouldn't miss any MEChA meetings—*we just went over the requirements last week*," Tina said with a frustrated tone in her voice.

"So, whose your favorite Chicano artist?" Paul asked Tina.

"I love Diego Rivera," Blanca replied.

"He doesn't qualify—he's Mexican. Besides, I was asking Tina. So, who's your favorite Chicano or Mexican-American artist? From north of the border, not south of the border," Paul asked again.

"God, leave her alone," Blanca told Paul, as she slapped him on the shoulder.

"I don't know. I hate art," Tina responded in a defensive tone.

"Well, then, based on your own definition, you're really not a Chicana, because you said, and I quote, 'Chicanos are proud of our culture.'"

"So what's your point, geek?" Tina asked.

"My point is, you can't be proud of your culture if you're not even *aware* of your culture—therefore, you can't be a Chicana," Paul responded.

"I like Magu," el chino said. "His style is energizing. I guess I'm more Chicano than you, Tina," Jinsoo said with a smile on his face.

Out of nowhere, we all heard a deep voice asking, "*What's going on here?*" It was as if Superman had suddenly landed behind us.

As it turned out, though, it was *El Chapulín Colorado* disguised as Ramon, saying, "*No contaban con mi astucia!*" (You weren't counting on my cunningness!)

53

Ramon must've sensed a Chicano in danger.

El Chapulín Colorado is a Mexican superhero—except he's not in very good shape, nor does he possess any impressive superhero powers. After all, how impressive can a superhero be wearing red tights, a yellow heart with "CH" in the middle of it, and antennas sticking out of his head? Not to mention the name, El Chapulín Colorado (The Red Grasshopper), isn't very intimidating.

"This fool doesn't think I'm a Chicana because I don't know any Chicano artists," Tina said, pointing at Paul. "And this fool," pointing at Jinsoo, "who talks slower than a snail, thinks he's a bad-ass Chicano because he likes Magu! *What the hell is a Magu,* anyway, fool?

"Aren't you majoring in British Literature?" Jinsoo asked Tina.

"That's right, fool—because Chicanas can study whatever the hell we want to," Tina responded. "You chinos say you're proud of your culture, but I don't see you guys majoring in Asian Studies—you guys are all into engineering and math, areas completely void of culture. You guys go to chino schools on the weekends, talk Korean to each other all the time, but have names like Cindy and Calvin! What the hell is that all about? Besides, what does my major have to do with anything?"

"Just because she doesn't know any Chicano artists, she can't be a Chicana?" Ramon asked Paul. "It's like saying you can't be Catholic if you don't know what Advent is about. And guess what? I'm sure Catholic churches are full on Sundays with people claiming to be Catholics, but most of them don't know what Advent is about. Should they be allowed to call themselves Catholics?"

I think Ramon has taken Professor Kepler's philosophy class as well.

"I didn't say she couldn't be a Chicana; she herself said she couldn't be one based on the definition she gave as to what constitutes a Chicana," Paul answered.

54

"Her lack of knowledge regarding Chicano artists just exemplifies how Chicano history and culture is neglected in the educational system. She, *we*, are victims of racist textbooks composed by racist, or at least by extremely naïve individuals who don't value our presence in this country enough to include us in the classroom textbooks," Ramon replied, as if he were giving a speech at a National MEChA Conference.

"*ÓRALE!*" Tina yelled out in agreement.

"All of that may be true, but based on her own definition, Tina still isn't a Chicana," Paul continued to insist.

Tina put one hand on her hip, and with the other hand she shook a finger in Paul's face while giving him a few choice words—it was Tina's version of the Socratic method.

I don't know what she said to him because I took off without saying a word. I was done contributing to discussions like this—I was all talked out.

For many years, though, I was consumed with these types of topics. I had a passion, a need to talk about issues like:

~ What's the difference between a Chicano and a Mexican-American?

~ Is the term Hispanic offensive?

~ If Mexicans want blacks to get over the whole "slavery issue," then why can't Mexicans get over the whole "Spanish conquest" issue?

~ In the novel, *Pocho*, did Richard sell out his people or do the right thing by leaving?

~ Who're the better parents: the white parents who want their kids to move out by age 20, or the Mexican parents who'll only let their kids move out when they get married?

~ Should one conform and change the system from within, or fight the system head on from the outside?

~ Are Mexicans segregated, or are we self-segregating?

~ Is illegal immigration something the government wants to control, or allow to continue so that companies can continue making huge profits?

~ Who's prouder of their race: a cholo or a Chicano Studies major?

But after so many opinions, after so much anger and frustration, after repeating the same lines and arguments over and over, I felt like the dialogue never progressed. This discussion can get no further than a hamster running on that wheel in its cage. Why? Because there will always be first-time freshmen entering college, all idealistic about how they're going to set society straight—as if they could wave a wand, say something magical that'll make society realize what's wrong, and make the necessary corrections.

I know, because I used to carry such a wand—until it took on the same weight as a damn cross, so I put it down years ago.

Now I only wave my individual wand. It's much lighter and a million times more effective.

As far as I'm concerned, concerning who is and who isn't a Chicano, if someone thinks he's a Chicano, then he's a Chicano.

Besides, it's not like we're dogs—there's no *Chicano Kennel Club* sending out Certificates of Authenticity or pedigree papers showing someone is a purebred Chicano.

There's no contest where Chicanos are walked around an arena and compete for the "Best in Show" Chicano.

Besides, what would a prize-winning Chicano look like, anyway?

Who'd be the judges?

Who'd appoint them as the judges?

If someone says he's a Chicano, then he's a Chicano. If someone named Gavin Fuentes lives in Beverly Hills, attends an elitist private school, plays the piano, hates soccer and tortillas, and says he's a Chicano—*then he's a Chicano.*

It's not like he's going to get busted for being an Undocumented Chicano. Besides, what's it to me? How's Gavin Fuentes identifying himself as a Chicano going to affect my life any?

And if someone does care, are there minimum requirements to being a Chicano? Who would set those requirements? Hell, who's going to enforce them?

As I was walking away from the group, I decided to go straight to the source regarding the Selection Committee—I turned and headed straight towards the Art Department to talk to Dr. Padilla myself.

THE MOTHERLAND

After walking across the campus, hiking up three flights of stairs, and going down a long narrow hallway, I discovered that Dr. Padilla wasn't even in his office.

According to the schedule posted on his door, he wouldn't be there for another hour, so I sat down on the floor to contemplate my next move.

As I sat there, Miranda, a girl I met in a history class last semester, walked up to me. While working on a group project together, we discovered that we were both born in the same small town in Mexico—Jalostotitlán. I love the fact that I was born in Jalos, short for Jalostotitlán. Miranda, on the other hand, doesn't like her place of origin at all.

When we first met, Miranda told me that she was born in San Diego. Right away I knew she was lying, because out of the thousands of Mexicans I know, none of them can prove that they were actually born in San Diego.

I've come to the realization that when Mexicans say they were born in San Diego, what they really mean is that they were born in Tijuana, Chula Vista, or some other place they're embarrassed about—like Bakersfield, for example.

Like my cousin Flor. She used to tell everyone that she was born in San Diego, when she was actually born in Tijuana—as if her birth place made her skin any lighter or diminished her slight chola accent.

Turns out, it wasn't so much that Miranda was ashamed of having been born in Jalos, as much as she was afraid of getting caught. Miranda is an illegal and is using her cousin's identity to attend college. She's a rare illegal, too; her Spanish isn't very good.

As for me, I've always loved the fact that I was born in Jalos. I remember in fourth grade, the first day of school, Mrs. Post had us introduce ourselves by saying our name and where we were born. It was all basic stuff, like my name is John, Gustavo, Nick, Leticia, Kim, or Andrew, and I was born in Anaheim, Fullerton, La Habra, or Orange.

These are the cities where the local hospitals are located. Those with insurance were most likely born at Saint Joseph's Hospital in Orange, or at Saint Jude's Hospital in Fullerton.

Ninety-nine percent of the people without insurance had their babies delivered at the La Habra Medical Clinic or in Anaheim at the Western Medical Hospital and Mental Health Center.

I find it interesting that the saints seem to be present only at the hospitals where the patients have insurance.

My brother thinks he's special because he was born at St. Joseph Hospital in Orange. He was born there, but not because my parents had insurance at the time. Rather, it was because my mother was riding the bus to her friend's house in Santa Ana, a city next to Orange, and she went into labor two months early. The bus driver called the fire department and she was taken to St. Joseph Hospital. And, in a sense, my brother is right—if you ask a few of his former teachers and the school psychologist, he sure is *special*.

When it came my turn to tell the class my name and where I was born, I was shaking with excitement.

"My name is Hector, and I was born in *Jalostotitlán, Jalisco, Mexico*."

I said it with as much passion as any proud, Green Card–carrying member could.

Silence engulfed the classroom. I knew the majority of them didn't know what the hell I had just said—just like we had no idea what the hell Wang Kim, the new student from Taiwan, had said earlier. We all knew he was excited—he had a big-ass smile

60

on his face the whole time he was talking, but we just couldn't understand what the hell he was so excited about.

Mrs. Post asked me to repeat myself a few more times, then she sent me up to the board to write the name down. I wrote it all in capital letters so it'd look more impressive: JÁLOSTOTITLÁN. I even placed an accent mark over both of the As to make it look more sophisticated. I knew it only went over one of the As, but I couldn't remember which one, so I accented both of them—after all, who the hell would know the difference in my class?

I looked like a genius up there writing a word down with 13 letters—a personal record. The funny thing was that I always got Ds on the spelling tests, and I was in a special reading program—but that day I felt as if I could've won a national spelling bee contest.

After school, I ran into Steve Hendrickson, the class bully, outside of Tommy's Arcade. He called me over. A few of his thug-friends were with him, and I thought they were going to take my pinball money. After walking up to them, Steve put his arm around my shoulder and said, "This is the guy that was born in that place with the weird name."

"Yeah?" one of his friends said. "That's crazy, man!"

"Say it," Steve said with a big smile on his face. I didn't hesitate to honor his request. Once, during lunch, Steve punched a guy in the nose because he didn't pass him the ketchup fast enough.

"Jalostotitlán, Jalisco, Mexico."

"Wwhhhaatt?" his short friend said slowly, with a distorted facial expression, as if he had just licked a lemon.

"That's nothing—listen to this. Say it with that crazy accent you used in class," Steve said.

"Jalostotitlán, Jalisco, Mexico!"

61

Steve's friends looked at each other with big eyes, they both gave me a high-five then took off on their Madrid skateboards.

His friends must have thought I was some kind of high-class world traveler, someone able to speak a mysterious language.

However, as proud as I am of saying I was born in Jalostotitlán, the truth of the matter is that I often feel extremely out of place there when I visit. I feel out of place there because my Spanish sucks.

I feel like a Montague crashing the Capulets' masquerade party every time I go to Jalos. I know I'm dressed like the other invited guests, but in my gut I know I'm completely out of place, that I shouldn't be there, like Romeo. I feel as if every time I open my mouth, the locals are able to see past the "mask" and realize that I'm an intruder.

I don't feel out of place with everyone, though, mostly with some of my cousin's friends. Most of the time they don't make fun of my Spanish, but when I mispronounce something really bad or say the wrong word, they can't stop laughing at me—they make me feel like an idiot.

I guess that's their way of demonstrating their "superiority" over me while they can, because they know that the next time I see them in el norte, those that speak a little bit of English will be taking my order at a Burger King drive-through, and those that don't speak any English at all will be washing, drying, and vacuuming my car at the Bubbles-R-Us Car Wash on Harbor Boulevard.

One time, one of my cousin's friends, Jose Luis, was on my case day after day. I didn't even want to hang out with my cousin anymore because I knew Jose Luis would be there.

Luck came my way when my aunt asked me if I wanted to go to Puerto Vallarta with her and her two kids. My uncle wasn't able to make it, so she offered me his spot. Who'd say no to a free trip to Puerto Vallarta?

We stayed at an all-inclusive hotel, something I'd never done before. It was great. All of the food and drinks were paid for, and the tips were already included. All I had to do was raise my hand, and the waitress would bring me a drink. During dinner a server was always standing next to the table, ready to grant any wish or desire we had. I didn't even have to get out of the pool to get a drink—there were servers everywhere.

The service was outstanding, but the best thing about the trip was that none of the hotel workers made fun of my Spanish—in front of me, at least. I was treated as if I were a fluent native speaker. I loved it.

At first, it felt a little weird being pampered so much. But after the second day, I was walking around the place as if I were a Kennedy from Boston, not a Zamora from La Habra.

I started believing that I deserved "to be treated like Royalty," as stated in the hotel's fancy brochures. My problem was that I took the brochures' propaganda, thus my sense of entitlement, back with me to Jalos.

When I got back to my grandmother's house, I walked out of the taxi and into the house—expecting my luggage to be brought in by someone, anyone. I was wrong.

After putting my own luggage down in the family room, I went straight to the dining room table, sat down, and asked my cousin Zoila to bring me a Coke. After flipping through the magazine that was on the table for a few seconds, I started wondering what the hell was taking so long with that Coke I had ordered.

"Zoil..." I didn't even get a chance to finish saying her name before she responded in an angry voice.

"Get your own pinche, Coke!" Zoila yelled out from the kitchen. She'd be a horrible resort employee.

I was initially appalled by the service in the house, but then I quickly realized that my Kennedy days were over.

Zoila is one of my favorite cousins, but I didn't think asking her to bring me a Coke was asking for too much. Especially considering what I had just done for her—I brought her a heavy-ass suitcase full of clothes from el norte.

Every time someone from el norte goes to Mexico, they're either obligated or guilt-ridden into taking clothes to family members down there. And every family has someone who determines who gets what—they play the role of the "Godfather," distributing the goods to the loyal family members.

In our family, the person who plays the role of the Godfather is my tía Chema. She'll sit down on the couch, and the suitcase with the newly arrived goods is placed on the coffee table in front of her. Instead of having a cigar in her hand, like a real Godfather, it's usually a torta or a bottle of Orange Fanta.

In a raspy voice, she'll say, *"Let's take a look at da' stuff."*

She'll then proceed to process the clothes. She'll check the blouses to see if all of the buttons are on, check the shirts for any rips, and, most importantly, she'll check the tags—Sears, Walmart, and JC Penny clothes go in one pile, while Ann Taylor, Macy's, and Nordstrom clothes that fit her are placed under the coffee table, where she keeps her private stash.

"You've done good," she always says to whoever brought her the suitcase and gives them a loving pat on the cheek.

There are three reasons why people from el norte send their clothes to Mexico.

Reason #1—The clothes are out of style, and the person giving away the clothes has finally accepted the fact that they will never come back in fashion. This is why Members Only jackets continue finding their way into Mexico.

Reason #2—The clothes no longer fit, and all attempts at dieting and exercising, real or imagined, have failed; therefore, all hope of ever fitting into the clothes again has been abandoned.

Reason #3—Someone died, and just as their heart and kidney can be transplanted into someone else, thus giving another person life, their clothes can also bring to life someone's sick and decaying wardrobe in Jalos. This was the type of clothing I had for Zoila—a dead girl's clothes, but a dead girl with a sense for fashion.

Mr. Robertson's daughter, from apartment H-8, was huge. She was 24 years old and must have weighed around 300 pounds. Kim was her name, and she died suddenly in her sleep. Usually, when one thinks of a 300-pound person, one pictures a person wearing baggy sweats.

But not Kim. She loved to design and sew her own clothes, even though she'd rarely leave the apartment. After she died, my mother "volunteered" to take all of Kim's clothes to the Goodwill Society.

Goodwill Society, my ass—more like the *Teresa Zamora Just Got Some Free Clothes Society.*

My mother does what all Mexican mothers do whenever they get clothes entrusted to them to either donate to charity or send to an orphanage in Mexico: First she looks through the clothes and keeps the good stuff for herself, just like my tía Chema.

This is why poor people in Mexico continue looking poor, despite the enormous amount of quality clothing being donated to them.

Mexican moms are no different than Mafia members—they both skim off the top before passing the goods on to the next level. The only difference is that Mafia members have bags of cash to show for their skimming, whereas Mexican mothers only have drawers full of blouses to show for their racketeering.

In this case, my tía Chema took one look at the size of the clothes that belonged to Kim, closed the suitcase and announced that it should be immediately taken to Zoila—a few more bowls of menudo, pozole, and a tray of pan dulce, and Zoila would be able to fit into poor Kim's clothes.

65

Zoila is so large that she can't share her clothes with any of her five sisters—I guess that's one advantage of being the biggest person in a petite family.

But before Zoila could wear any of the clothing in Jalos, it first had to be delivered to her all the way from La Habra. And I was the fool that delivered the suitcase. I carried it ...

~ from our apartment, to the car

~ from the car, to the check-in counter at the Los Angeles airport

~ from the luggage-claim area in Guadalajara airport, to the bus terminal

~ from the bus stop area in Jalos, to my tía Chema's house

~ from my tia's house, to Zoila's house.

... and she still had the nerve to tell me to get my own *pinche* Coke? I swear, some people have no sense of reciprocity.

On the other hand, the night before I got back home from Puerto Vallarta, Zoila did pump the bedroom I was staying in full of a bunch of DDT to kill off the mosquitoes and any other living creatures that were in the room. A few more pumps, and I'm sure I would've been one of the casualties.

I must've been bitten more than a billion times during the first night I was there.

Although banned in the United States, DDT is the pesticide of choice in Mexico. My relatives spray that stuff all over the house as if it were holy water and the mosquitoes were evil spirits.

I find it very interesting that Mexican Nationals, among other groups, protested against the use of DDT in the United States in the '70s, but yet they still use it regularly in their own homes in Mexico.

I think a little DDT would be a good thing in the United States. The whole time I was in Mexico, I didn't see a single cockroach at the house or at the restaurants. Yet, the last time I ate at my favorite hamburger place in La Habra, *Hamburgers de Sinaloa*, I saw a cockroach walking off with one of my onion rings as I returned from the restroom. I think the damn thing was even smiling at me as it dunked the onion ring in some ketchup before jumping off the table and onto the floor.

I'm seriously thinking of not going back to that hamburger joint for a long time. Maybe I'll go to *Pedro's Hamburguesas*—I hear they make a great pastrami sandwich there.

A trick I learned in Mexico, as far as not getting sick, is to find something that won't get me sick, and keep on eating it day after day. This last time I was in Jalos, I went to a torta shop next to the plaza: *Tortas Malibu Estilo*.

I didn't order anything from the main menu.

~ I don't like cabeza—meat from the head of a roasted cow.

~ Sesos was never going to be an option for me. Who in their right mind would want to eat a calf's brain? A full-grown cow's brain, maybe, but not a baby cow's brain—that's just wrong.

~ Tripas smelled good, but there is just something unhealthy about the thought of eating the intestines of a cow, unless it's menudo, of course.

~ I used to love lengua as a kid. My mother told me lengua was the soft part of a cow. I didn't give it much thought—I just knew I loved lengua.

Then, when I was about 10 years old, I saw a big-ass lengua in the meat department, and just about threw up on the spot realizing that when we sat around the dinner table eating lengua, we were actually eating a cow's tongue! *Who eats cow's tongue?* I don't think that even the chinos eat that!

There was also the basic carnitas, carne asada, and chicken.

Everyone says the tortas there are great, but I like to be extremely conservative with my food selection in Mexico. I wish

I could eat the food from any street vendor, but I have a weak stomach. I even get sick to my stomach when my Coco Puffs sits in the bowl of milk for too long.

Tortas Malibu Estilo has a great meat department for the locals, but it's the crema (sour cream) that put this eatery on the map. People come from all over to have the crema placed on their tortas. There's always a line outside, as if it were the day after Thanksgiving and the shoppers are dying to get into the store to buy their Christmas presents.

As tempting as all of the food there was, I knew most of those things would get me sick, so I stuck to an American classic: a grilled cheese sandwich.

When I first ordered the grilled cheese, it caused a lot of confusion behind the counter—as if I was Jesus overturning the money-changing tables at the Temple. The three girls behind the counter didn't know what to do with my order because they were set in their ways as to how to go about preparing a torta.

The first girl was in charge of putting the meat in the torta. She'd then pass the torta on to the next girl, who'd add the onions, tomatoes, jalapeños, and anything else the customer wanted. Ninety percent of the tortas were ordered *con todo*—with everything.

The last girl would then spread the famous crema in the torta, then brush some melted butter on the outside of the bread and place the whole thing on the grill, giving it a nice crisp taste.

And here I came along.

"I'd like a grilled cheese sandwich, please."

The girls looked at each other, unsure of what to do next.

I then explained to them that I wanted a slice of yellow cheese placed between two pieces of sandwich bread, not torta bread, and then grilled.

They proceeded to move with caution. The first girl looked around for the sandwich bread. She found a loaf under some napkins and smelled it for freshness.

"No meat?" she asked.

"No thank you." She then slowly passed the two pieces of bread to the second girl, perplexed as to why someone wouldn't want a calf's brain or a cow's tongue placed between the plain pieces of bread.

"No tomatoes?" asked the second girl.

"No thank you"

"No onions or jalapeños?"

"No thank you."

"Cabbage?"

"No thank you."

"Avocados?"

"No. Just a slice of cheese," I said, pointing to the block of cheese on the counter behind her. She turned around, cut off a piece of cheese and placed it in between the bread. She then handed it over to the third girl very slowly, as if it were a bomb that could detonate at any second.

That's when the "sacrilegious" moment took place. The third girl placed the sandwich in her left hand, and with her right hand she reached for the spatula in the jar of crema. She was about to spread crema on the sandwich, when I stuck my head over the counter and quietly said-

"No crema, please. Grilled cheese sandwiches don't have crema."

All three of the girls looked at me in disbelief, as if they couldn't believe what they had just heard. I noticed a few of the customers whispering to one another. I think one customer even stood up and walked out after realizing what was going on.

The three girls huddled up. Finally, the girl in charge of the bread and meat section said, "Let me get this straight. You want sandwich bread, not a bolillo?"

"Correct."

"You just want a slice of cheese?"

"Correct."

"No tomatoes, no avocados, no onions?"

"Nothing, just the bread and cheese."

"*Not even crema?*" she asked me with a tone in her voice as if she had just asked her boyfriend if he had been cheating on her, knowing that the answer was going to be "yes."

"Correct, not even crema," I responded in a manner whereby I tried to convey to her that my rejecting the crema had nothing to do with her, but me—I was the one with the issues.

The crema-and-butter girl composed herself enough to ask me one final question, "Do you want butter on the outside of the bread before placing it on the grill?"

I wasn't sure how to respond. Obviously a grilled cheese sandwich needs butter on the outsides before being grilled, but my first instinct was to say "no," just because I hadn't asked around to find out if the butter would get me sick.

But then I felt like I had disappointed the three girls enough for one day—I didn't want to hurt their feelings anymore. I slowly nodded my head in the affirmative: I would gladly accept the butter on the outside of the bread.

The three girls let out a slight sigh of relief, as if I had let them know that I wasn't the monster they had thought I was, after all.

Once the sandwich had done its time on the grill, I sat down to eat. The three girls didn't take their eyes off of me the whole time I ate my grilled cheese sandwich.

Little do they know that if they ever cross the border and get a job at Hamburgers de Sinaloa in La Habra, they'll become experts in preparing grilled cheese sandwiches.

I was glad that I went through all of that hassle because I didn't get sick. However, I had to go through the whole charade again three days later when the first three girls got the day off, and a new set of girls showed up to work. Two days later I was sick. I don't know if it was the grilled cheese sandwich from the new girls or the menudo my cousin Zoila made. Either way, it was time to go home.

And this is the most depressing part of taking a trip to Mexico—the voyage home.

It's depressing, not because I'm leaving Mexico, but rather because I'm reentering the world and its problems.

When I'm in Mexico, I don't watch television, listen to the radio, or read the newspaper. My ignorance of the world's problems makes the world a wonderful place. When I'm in Mexico, there're no murderers, famines or terrorists—being in denial has its mental benefits.

But once I'm at the airport, I buy the newspaper and reality returns—terrorism, floods, serial killers, droughts, corruption, the Yankees in first place, and all kinds of other inhumane things are taking place all over the world.

The only good part about returning home is that I no longer feel like I'm pretending. It feels really good to be able to speak English again, not worrying about if I'm using the right tense or mispronouncing words in Spanish—God knows I have a hard enough time getting that stuff right in English. Once I'm back at home, I'm no longer a pocho, but a Mexican-American—the masquerade party is over.

On the airplane back home this summer, I helped my aunt generate a list of things my little cousins wouldn't be able to do anymore once they got back to the United States. They'd no longer be able to...

#1 Ride in the back of a pick-up truck

#2 Leave the top five buttons of their shirts unbuttoned

#3 Wear three gold necklaces at the same time

#4 Drink Orange Fanta for breakfast, lunch, and dinner

#5 Say "cabron" or "pendejo" in every sentence

#6 Wear the same shirt for three days in a row

"I heard you went to Jalos recently," Miranda asked me as she slid down on the floor to sit next to me. "How'd it go?"

"How'd it go? Have you ever heard of anybody coming back from a trip there saying, 'that place sucks'? It was fun. When're you going down there?"

"I'm taking a Spanish class right now to brush up on my Spanish. I hear they're brutal down there if you sound all stupid in Spanish," she replied.

"If you want to improve your Spanish, listen to Mexican music. That'll help you more than a Spanish class. Nobody in Jalos is going to ask you to spell anything or ask you where the accent marks go," I said.

"Is that what you did?"

"Yeah, and it helped me. I also kept a folder and wrote down all of the Spanish words I didn't understand and translated them into English."

"Wow, you must of talked like a local down there."

"Oh, no, they ripped me apart a lot of the times. But it did help, somewhat," I said.

I then heard some footsteps down the hall. I thought it was going to be Dr. Padilla, but instead it was another student looking for another professor. I looked at my watch and realized that Dr. Padilla probably wasn't going to make it to his office hours. Perhaps he got caught up in a meeting somewhere.

I had nothing else to do until my evening class. I really needed to study for the test we were going to be given because I wasn't doing well in the class. It was a cultural anthropology class, and it sounded very interesting when I read the course description. As it turned out, it's a boring class.

Going to that class is kind of like going to church on Sundays. I don't always pay attention to the priest when he's talking or when the scriptures are being read. Often, I'm thinking about what to do later that day, what I should eat for lunch, or what I'll do once I win the lottery.

We're all like that in church—we look like we're paying attention, but we're really daydreaming, big time.

It's the same thing in class. I'm looking at the professor lecturing, but I'm thinking about everything else in the world. When he looks my way, I pretend to write some notes down, just as I nod my head in agreement with the priest when he looks my way.

Miranda went off to her Spanish class, and I decided to take off to Tavo's house, a friend I've had since seventh grade. Actually, it's his parents' house. Mexicans never move out unless they get married, and 42% of the time the newlyweds move into one of the parents' garage to save money.

There aren't a whole lot of 20 or 30-year-old single Mexicans living on their own. And there certainly aren't any 40 or 50-year-olds living on their own. By the time they're that old, they're either taking care of their parents or no longer see any practical reason for moving out.

I've heard rumors that there're some single, older Mexicans living out there on their own, but I think it's just a legend—like la Llorona

My friend, Tavo, converted the garage into a big bedroom. Everyone calls it Tavo's Cave, or The Cave, for short.

73

Everybody loves hanging out there. That's where we watch football and baseball games or just listen to Tavo's stereo system while doing nothing productive at all.

We've all known each other since Little League, and we always have each other's backs. Tavo's Cave is like...

~ the bar from *Cheers*.

~ Mel's Diner from *Happy Days*.

~ the bar scene in *Star Wars*.

It's home away from home, except for Tavo, of course—it is his home.

The Cave is the first place you go if you hooked up with a girl so you can brag about it, but it's also the first place you go if a girlfriend dumped you. If you got a new job, you bring a six-pack to celebrate. If you got fired, you bring a twelve-pack for the celebration. If nothing is going on in your life, Tavo's Cave is the destination until something comes up.

I guess Tavo's Cave is like purgatory: We hang out there in limbo until there's somewhere better to go, yet it's still better than being home alone.

TAVO'S CAVE

There were several cars parked along the street as I pulled up to Tavo's Cave.

It's kind of like Plato's Cave, but without the shadows.

Tavo's old gray Ford F-150 truck was parked in the driveway. It's always there. Tavo has it made living at home with his parents—they pay for his gas and car insurance, he doesn't pay any rent, he gets an allowance, his mother cooks his meals, cleans his room, does his laundry, and probably wipes his ass when he's done taking a crap.

Actually, except for the wiping-the-ass-part, most Mexican mothers do that stuff for their sons—the daughters have to fend for themselves. The daughters eventually grow up, however, and take out the resentment they held towards their spoiled brothers-on their husbands.

Life is pretty good for Tavo, except for when it comes to girlfriends—the poor bastard has never had one. Besides his own inability to get a girl, nobody wants to set him up for two reasons.

The first reason is because he's a loser. I don't want to set him up with any of my cousins—not even with my fat-ass cousin Zoila. Tavo is 23 years old, doesn't have a job, doesn't have any ambition, and his truck doesn't even have seatbelts. So, in a way, if I did set him up with Zoila, I'd technically be putting her life in danger. I couldn't do that with a clear conscience—even though Zoila has never met a seatbelt she can buckle.

The second reason is because we don't want him to have a girlfriend. If he gets one, we'll have to find a new place to hang out, and none of us have our own bedroom—we all share a room with a brother or two. Besides, Tavo seems okay without having a girlfriend, too—life is pretty good for him at 493 Clifton Drive.

Gilbert, the self-described rebel, was also there. He drives an old 1978 yellow Chevy Camaro that's needed a new paint job since 1982, and a new muffler since '85.

He doesn't want to put any money into that car because he's saving up for his dream car—a yellow 1969 Camaro. Gilbert is horrible at saving money, though. As soon as he saves a little, he takes off to Vegas, Laughlin, or Husson's Cantina in Ensenada. Hell, at least he likes to travel.

Gilbert installs residential garage doors for a company located in La Puente. He's thought of starting his own construction company someday, but he'd first have to get his contractor's license. He's had the brochure, *Become a Contractor in Six Easy Steps,* sitting in the back seat of his car for the past 6 months.

~ He's had the - *Become an Air Conditioning and Heating Repair Man* brochure for a year.

~ He's had the - *Become an Electrician* brochure for 2 years.

~ In the glove compartment, the - *Learn How to be an Elevator Technician* brochure can be found.

Tavo says Gilbert keeps the brochures in the car to trick the girls he dates into thinking he's an ambitious, self-motivated entrepreneur.

Tavo is just jealous of Gilbert, though. The truth is, Tavo copied Gilbert's "trick" recently; he put some brochures in his truck. He even got a *Become a Dental Technician* brochure—he thought it'd look impressive if the girls thought he was in the medical field.

His plan never worked, though, because he lacked Gilbert's "smooth-talking" ways. Tavo was never able to get a girl in the truck to see the broachers because his pick-up lines are even worse than mine.

76

"Do you wanna check out my brochures in the truck, baby?" doesn't do it for the ladies. As a matter of fact, a while ago he freaked a girl out so much that she called the cops on him—I told him it wasn't a good idea to wear sunglasses and a red beanie to nightclubs. He thought they'd add "a sense of intrigue and mystery" to his persona. Instead, he looked more like a pervert than a man of mystery.

Fred was also there. "Fred" is what happens to highly intelligent fourth-generation Chicanos who don't go to college. He has a massive chip on his shoulder and a negative attitude, and he's the most bitter person I know. He feels the world is against him, and his mission in life is to not be taken advantage of by anyone—real or imagined.

One time Fred read a research paper I was working on. I had left it in the back seat, and he asked if he could take a look at it as we drove to the park to play some basketball. After parking the car, he said things like, "Shouldn't there be a semicolon here instead of a colon?" and "Shouldn't it say, 'whom' instead of 'who'?"

I just responded by saying, "It's a lot easier *to be a critic than an author*, isn't it?"

He got pissed and said, "All that schooling is just going to get you a piece of paper, bro. That's all a college diploma is—a piece of paper."

As it turned out, he was right. I should've used a semicolon, and it was "whom" instead of "who." But I'm the one that got the B- on the paper, not him. And ...

~ *I'm the one* that's going to have the "piece of paper" hanging in a cheap frame in my mother's hall.

~ *I'm the one* who'll be able to apply for jobs he doesn't qualify for, and get promotions he'll only dream of.

~ *I'm the one* who'll live in a better neighborhood.

~ *I'm the one* who'll have quality health insurance for his family.

77

~ *I'm the one* who'll look around and be amazed and appreciative of what the world has to offer.

I know it's not just a piece of paper, and so does Fred. He's too smart to minimize a college degree as "just a piece of paper." I think Fred is just too insecure to give college a try—like Gilbert is too afraid of actually dialing a number on one of his many brochures.

Fred is a critic. Fred is a back-seat driver. Fred is a Monday-morning quarterback. He'll never have the balls it takes to write down his own thoughts or opinions.

Fred hates too many things to ever be happy or ambitious. One particular item of interest on his long list are white people. Fred hates them because he thinks they're all racists—yet he doesn't think that hating all white people is racist.

Actually, Fred doesn't hate all white people—he has "a thing" for blonde girls. He justifies dating white girls, to himself, by saying he's just trying to get back at "the man." He says his goal in life is to get as many white dads pissed off as he can. Fred doesn't give himself enough credit, though—he could piss off any father, regardless of his race, by dating his daughter.

Illegals are also on Fred's list of things he hates, and he can barely stomach first-generation Mexican-Americans, like myself.

He thinks we're collecting the fruits of his ancestor's labor— that we, the illegals and "first-generation wetbacks," as he calls us, are blind to the struggles, protests, court cases, and all of the battles against the establishment that have taken place in order to make things better for Mexicans in the United States.

He says we come blindly into this country believing the myth that *all men are created equal* and that *America is the land of opportunity*. He says we're blind to the oppression and racism that has prevented people of color from moving up the socioeconomic ladder for hundreds of years.

And he may have a point. Many first-generation Mexican-Americans are naïve about the abuses of the past. We have first-generation dads telling us about how we need to work hard and get an education in order to live a better life, while fourth-generation Chicanos, like Fred, have dads and grandfathers telling them stories about...

~ being hit by teachers for speaking Spanish in school

~ being pulled over by cops for no reason

~ being denied the use of public swimming pools

~ being denied the right to vote

~ being denied a job because of their race

~ being put in the frontlines of war

and more stories about

~ not being allowed to move into certain neighborhoods

~ not being allowed to take college prep classes

~ not being allowed to be buried in certain cemeteries

So, yeah, I guess there may be some credibility to Fred's point of view.

Alfonso was sitting on the couch when I walked in, staring at the floor. Alfonso is always there, especially since his girlfriend broke up with him a couple of weeks ago. At first we all felt bad for the guy, but we've gotten over it—now he's just annoying. Alfonso has been feeling sorry for himself, and he wants the world to feel sorry for him, too. It's not surprising, though; he's always been that way.

If someone has a headache, Alfonso has a migraine. If someone breaks a finger, Alfonso has rheumatoid arthritis. If someone gets a speeding ticket, Alfonso says he's going to be audited by the IRS.

He wants everyone to think something like - "I thought I had it bad, but poor Alfonso, he has it worse."

79

And we do think this way—sort of. But it's more like, "Our lives could be worse—we could be Alfonso."

George was looking through Tavo's CD collection. His real name is Jorge, but he prefers George. George says he's tired of people pronouncing his name as *Whore-Hey*. Fred gives him a hard time for going with the name George, instead of Jorge – even though Fred's real name is Alfredo. But that's usually how bitter people like Fred are: hypocrites.

George never complains about anything, even though he has good reasons to complain. His parents recently got divorced. His back has been messed up since his car accident last year. He has a crappy job—he drives grouchy old people to their doctor's appointments. However, he sees life as an enjoyable ride in which things will always get better—he'd make a good Hindu.

What I love about hanging out at the cave is that everybody talks nothing but bullshit all of the time. I give my mom a hard time for always talking with her comadres about insignificant crap, but we're no different in The Cave.

One time I heard my mother talking with her comadres for over an hour about what color blouse is more appropriate to wear to church—blue or red?

My mother is a blue-blouse supporter. I heard her telling the ladies in the kitchen that red was an offensive color to wear to church because red symbolizes the fires of hell. Her comadres agreed by nodding their heads up and down, like bobblehead dolls. She went on to explain how the color red also symbolizes blood, as in the ancient human sacrifices conducted by the Aztecs—thus making the color sacrilegious in church.

One of the ladies chimed in by saying that blue is the appropriate color to wear because blue symbolizes the heavens and the holy water used during baptisms.

I didn't hang around listening to this stuff for an hour. I know they talked about it that long because I took off to Ollie's Liquor Store to get some munchies, and when I got back, an hour later, they were still on the topic—and they were still bobbing their heads up and down.

This is what comadres end up talking about when they give up novelas (soap operas) for Lent.

I don't think we're as bad as my mother and her comadres, but give us time—we're only in our early twenties.

Cave Talk

~ Mario and his wife had their baby yesterday—a boy.

~ What'd they name him? Mario Junior Junior?

~ No, fool, they named him Zula!

~ *Zula*? What's that? Some Aztec god?

~ They named him after *Tamazula*!

~ What?

~ As in the hot sauce, Tamazula?

~ Is there any other type of Tamazula that you know of, fool?

~ They call him Zula for short.

~ At least they didn't name him after the hot sauce, El Pato (The Duck). In Cuba, el pato means, "he's gay."

~ We're not in Cuba, fool.

~ I went to Mexico a while ago, and they put Tapatio *on their popcorn*! I loved it—especially with tons of butter.

~ My cousin puts mayonnaise on her corn!

~ Don't all you wetbacks put mayonnaise on your corn?

~ I hate going to Mexico.

~ Why?

~ It drives me nuts.

~ Like, what?

~ Like every time you walk by someone, they say *adiós* to you, and you have to say *adiós* back to them, otherwise they'll think you're rude.

~ I wish my girl didn't say adiós to me.

~ Up and down the street, all you hear is adiós, adiós, adiós, adiós. And I learned that when you say adiós, you have to tilt your head down, not up.

~ What's the difference?

~ When you tilt your head down, you're being courteous. When you tilt your head up and say adiós, you're being arrogant.

~ Is there a handbook for all this etiquette crap?

~ Dude, have a shirt printed with "adios" on it, and just point to the shirt as you walk by them—you won't have to say adiós ever again.

~ That's stupid.

~ I thought adios meant goodbye?

~ It does. But it can also be used to say hello.

~ Kind of like aloha and shalom?

~ I guess. I've never been to Hawaii or New York City.

~ When you were in Cancun, did you go to Chichen Itza?

~ *Chichen Itza?* No, I didn't hear about that club. Mostly, we went to The Hard Rock Café and Señor Frogs.

~ That's not what I meant, idiot.

~ Seriously? He thinks Chichen Itza is a club?

~ The last time I went to Mexico, they had to stop the plane at Mexicali to get more fuel. They didn't let us get up to use the restrooms for over an hour.

~ Refuel? What the hell? Why wouldn't the plane have enough fuel in the first place to fly from Guadalajara to Los Angeles?

~ Because the plane was being flown by a Mexican pilot, and you know Mexicans-we never fill up the tank with gas.

~ So why couldn't you use the toilets?

~ They said that if we flush the toilet while the plane was refueling, it could set off a spark and start a fire—something about static electricity, I think.

~ What the hell? Were you guys pissing gas or cheap tequila?

~ Man, thanks for the heads up. I'm putting on some of my grandfather's diapers next time I fly.

~ Those things work!

~ How would you know?

~ I, well, *I've heard* they work.

~ You tried one, didn't you?

~ *Hell, yeah!* I didn't have to get up once to go to the bathroom.

~ My cousin just got back from Mexico. He's all sad.

~ Why's that?

~ Remember my cousin, Mazatl Costi?

~ What about him?

~ He changed his name to Julian.

~ What? Why?

~ Because he found out that his Indian name, Mazatl Costi, actually means "Yellow Butterfly." He thinks the name is too feminine.

~ *He thinks* it's too feminine? Dude, if *he thinks* it's too feminine, *he is* too feminine.

~ Damn, he went from being Geronimo and Sitting Bull to Peter Pan.

~ He should've just kept his name.

~ Hey, just because you could live with a feminine name, *Guadalupe*, it doesn't mean everyone else can.

~ Seriously? *Guadalupe* is your middle name? Any name is better than *Guadalupe*.

~ Even "el pato."

~ Speaking of messed-up names, I work with a short, dark Mexican named Joe Smith.

~ Yeah, right.

~ I swear to God! Well his real name is Josue, but he goes by Joe. But his last name is Smith, and he barley speaks English.

~ I know a Mexican named Hans Scheunemann. Poor bastard—he can't even pronounce his own last name right.

~ Can you just imagine that short dark Mexican dude getting pulled over by a cop, and the cop asking him his name? "My name is Joe Smith, señor." "What's your real name, *Pedro*?" "It's Joe Smith, I promise, señor." "Get out of the car and spread your legs, now!"

~ How come you didn't show up to the basketball game the other day?

~ My girlfriend's friend's cousin's neighbor died—and we went to the funeral.

~ I was wondering why you seemed so shaken up lately. Sorry for your loss.

~ Oh, I didn't even know the guy.

~ I know. I was just being sarcastic, fool.

~ Anyway, they buried the guy up high in a wall, not in the ground.

~ It's called a mausoleum crypt.

~ Call it what you want. All I know is I'd never want to be buried in one of those things.

~ Why not? I think they're pretty cool.

~ *Hell, no!* I want people to be able to lay flowers down by my tombstone, and not have to throw the flowers up some 30 feet and hope they stick on a handle way up on the man-o-lium.

~ Mausoleum.

~ Whatever!

~ How cute. You want flowers brought to you.

~ I'm sure they got ladders there for those up that high.

~ Being buried in a wall seems too industrial.

~ I don't see it as industrial. I see it as modern.

~ I just hope there's someone around that loves me enough to bury me.

~ I doubt there will be, fool, so start saving your money-because nobody else is going to wanna bury your sorry ass.

~ So I'm thinking of getting my contractor's license.

~ Don't start with that crap again.

~ Come on, let the boy dream a little.

85

~ I'd rather hear more about Alfonso's break-up.

~ Seriously, this month I'm going to...

~ I think she'd take me back if I promised to ...

~ She ain't taking you back! Get over it.

~ Stop biting your nails.

~ I'm not. I'm cleaning them.

~ Hey, did you get that promotion you wanted, Fred?

~ They gave it to a guy who I'm pretty sure is working with a fake Social Security Card. He knows Spanish and can tell all the wetbacks in the warehouse what to do. However, if our company would *follow the law*, I would've gotten the promotion.

~ Why? Because of Affirmative Action?

~ No, fool, because the guy is illegal.

~ Oh, that reminds me. My cousin is looking for a job. Can you hook him up? He should be here from Mexico next week.

~ Next week? Is he only halfway across the desert?

~ So, did you get the job or not?

~ Screw you.

~ *Mira este pinche, culo. Él es smart, trabaja* hard, *merece el* promotion (Look at this ass. He's intelligent, works hard, and deserves the promotion).

~ Whatever, dude; go ahead and talk crap about me. Screw you and your Spanish.

~ That's funny.

~ Carlos Fuentes once said, "Monolingualism is curable."

86

~ Is that the guy who sat next to us in Biology class?

~ You're an idiot.

~ Let's get going.

~ Where?

~ Dude, I told you. We're going to that new club in Riverside to celebrate my birthday.

~ That's why we're going? Since when do we celebrate each other's birthdays?

~ No kidding-mine was last week and you guys didn't tell me nothing.

~ I told you about this last week, fool.

~ I can't go.

Silence.

And just like that, the elephant walked in the room—I was going to college and they weren't. Why else wouldn't I go with them to the new club? They knew I had a night class.

We never talked about college in Tavo's Cave. There was another group I'd hang out with back in high school once in a while, and they were all applying to major universities. It was a natural progression for them—they had been in GATE, Honors classes and AP classes. Paul Mendez was even offered a full scholarship to Stanford. Mark was hoping to get into Columbia, and Chris was hoping to get admitted into UCLA-and eventually they both got their wishes.

I liked to ask them questions about where they were applying, if they were going to live in the dorms, what they were going to major in, and stuff like that.

They'd occasionally ask me where I planned on going to college, but they were only being nice—they knew I was taking

87

Algebra One and a typing class my senior year in high school. My schedule didn't exactly scream, "future college graduate."

I knew all along, ever since I could remember, that I was going to go to college, though. I guess I wasn't too worried about applying to universities or getting good grades because I knew I'd be going to Fullerton College, like my older brother and sister.

It never even occurred to me to take the SAT test. While others were stressed out about being accepted in this university or that university, I was content knowing that I'd be accepted into Fullerton College — after all, they accept everyone.

I did, however, have the foresight to swallow my pride and enroll in Algebra One and a typing class my senior year. I knew I was going to college, but I also knew I didn't know the answer to $5x + 12 - 34 = y$, therefore, what does x equal, if y equals 23?

I had the misfortune, or fortune at the time, of taking Mr. Keen for ninth-grade Pre-Algebra, and having him again for tenth-grade Algebra One. Mr. Keen was a few years away from retiring or dying, so teaching wasn't his priority. He was also an Air Force veteran. A good way to get him mad was to tell him that the Marines are more important to national security than the Air Force.

He'd then go off on a tangent explaining the role of the Air Force and how they made it possible for the Marines to carry out their missions. And before we'd know it, the bell would ring and it'd be another day without learning a damn thing.

After 2 years of not learning anything from Mr. Keen, I was off to geometry. Talk about not having a chance in hell of passing a class.

I had no idea what was going on in there. Mr. Foster gave us quizzes with all kinds of geometry crap on the page. There were angles here and angles there, and I didn't have the slightest idea how to go about solving the problems. And to make matters even worse, there wasn't anyone sitting around me to copy off of—

they all covered their answer sheets like a mother covers her child in a rainstorm.

To kill time in class, I'd convert the angles on the page into ramps, and then draw motorcycles jumping off of them. I also got pretty good at converting the angles into airplanes. After a couple of weeks of this, I knew I was in serious danger of not even getting a D in the class.

Although I've only gotten just a few As in my academic career, I've never gotten an F. Strangely, this was something I took pride in, and I wanted to keep this streak alive.

One day, I had a brilliant idea—an idea I thought was a win-win for everyone. I told Mr. Foster I'd stop attending class and bothering the other students if he'd give me a W at the end of the semester. A W would be a lot better than an F, because a W wouldn't factor into my GPA. Mr. Foster just rubbed his chin and said, "Let me think about it, Hector."

I didn't show up to class the rest of the semester. I hung out with people in the parking lot, I'd go to the donut shop, I took naps in my friends' cars-I basically hung out with anyone who didn't understand what the hell was going on in their second-period class, either.

Before I knew it, the end of the semester was up, and I received a W on my report card. I was so excited that I went back to Mr. Foster to see if we could keep the same arrangement for the next semester.

Once again, he rubbed his chin and said, "Let me think about it, Hector." And, once again, I got a W in the class. As it turned out, that semester I got my highest GPA ever in high school—it was 2.80, baby! That was counting my A in PE and the A I got for being a teacher's aid for PE. Not having a math class really improved my academic status.

So, after 3 years of math at La Habra High School, I had a D in Pre-Algebra, a D in Algebra One, and a W in Geometry. I *obviously* I had a promising academic future ahead of me.

I had a choice to make: either enter college not understanding the math that a smart fourth grader knows, or swallow my pride and ask my counselor to place me in Mr. Rule's Algebra class my senior year. I heard that he could teach anybody math. I'll admit, it was embarrassing being the only senior in the math class, but it turned out being a great move on my part.

To this date, Mr. Rule is one of the best teachers I've ever had. He didn't turn me into a math major—I still don't like math—but he made me understand it. He wasn't a military veteran, so I couldn't throw him off the topic with that. He wasn't a sports buff, so there wasn't any Dodgers or Lakers talk going on. When the bell rang, he taught us math—and I got it, I understood it.

After my math class, I'd walk down the hall to my typing class. I felt like a giant among the freshmen surrounding me. The funny thing was, they'd always ask me what university I was planning on attending next year! Cute bastards—if only they knew.

My parents always encouraged us to go to college. My father would always say, "Get an education, so you won't have to work like a burro, like me."

Santiago, my oldest brother, was the first one to attend college. He's a very smart guy—it seemed like the natural thing for him to do. He eventually earned a Bachelor's Degree in Philosophy at Cal State Fullerton.

However, he didn't just major in philosophy; he lives it. He spends all of his time reading and writing about it. Having his nose in a book all day long drives my father nuts-it even gets him angry.

I think the problem is that my father is a blue-collar worker. What I mean is, at the end of the day, blue-collar workers have something to show after a hard day's work. My father picked lemons when he first came to the United States. After a 10-hour shift, he had hundreds of pounds of lemons in sacks to show for his effort. Now that he works in a food distribution warehouse, he can see the dozens of pallets he has put together containing 40-pound sacks of sugar, 20-pound sacks of coffee, 5-gallon drums of cooking oil, and other stuff needed to supply a restaurant.

On the other hand, my brother doesn't have anything to show after reading Plato's *The Republic* or Kant's *Critique of Pure Reason*. The knowledge and critical analysis is in my brother's head, and that can't be placed on a scale like a sack of lemons to be weighed or placed on a pallet to be shipped to restaurants throughout California and Nevada. This is, I think, what frustrates my father.

My sister was the next one to go to college. She was also smart—and mad. We all thought she'd become a lawyer. But to everyone's surprise, she transferred to Cal State Fullerton as a business major. Now she's a semester away from graduating— again.

Truth is, she's been a semester away from graduating for three years now. She did the worst thing any college student could do—she got a full-time job, and soon afterwards she bought a brand-new car.

Since she was so close to graduating, she figured she could handle the last three classes she needed by taking them at night. She lasted about a month. After working all day, the last thing she wanted to do was to attend a 3-hour lecture, three times a week.

Several years have passed, but she still hasn't found the time to complete the classes. She has, however, found plenty of time to party with her friends after work.

My other brother joined the Air Force after high school. He was the rebel in the family. He got kicked out of La Habra High School his sophomore year for fighting and cutting too many classes. He'd fight anybody: cholos, surfers, chinos, punk rockers-he even had it out with a few honor roll students along the way. He eventually graduated from a continuation school.

And to this day, whenever we all watch Jeopardy together, he kicks all of our butts.

By the time I got out of high school, my older siblings had already cleared a path to higher education. This kind of made it tough on me. I had no excuses to fall back on—they had removed them all. I couldn't make the following excuses as to why I couldn't go to college:

~ Nobody in my family has ever gone to college

~ I don't have any role models

~ My parents don't support me going to college

~ I have no idea on how to go about registering

~ I'm Mexican

It's tough being the third person in the family to attend college—no excuse works.

When I first started college, my brother gave me two bits of advice. The first tip was to get to know the college catalog. He told me that the counselors, even though they don't mean to, often screw up on the advice they give.

My brother's counselor told him to enroll in a certain class, but it turned out he didn't need the class, and when he went to add the class he did need, it was already closed and the instructor didn't add him. My brother was pissed, and that's when he decided to take matters in his own hands—he never entered a counselor's office again. Santiago was able recite the college catalog better than a born-again Christian could recite passage John 3:16 from the Bible.

The other tip he gave me was to be selfish. What he meant was to put my education first, if I really want to graduate. He told me about the fights that he and my parents would sometimes go through because he had to study for a test or finish a report for school, and therefore wouldn't be able to attend a baptism or a birthday party. I never really paid much attention to their fights—I just figured he didn't want to go to whatever event was going on at the time.

But those arguments were nothing compared to the crap my friends are going to give me, he explained. Peer pressure is a leading cause as to why people drop out of college, according to my brother.

I guess I had better friends than my brother had because I never got into arguments or felt the pressure to put my friends ahead of my education.

They never told me...

~ fine, don't hang out with us, college boy

~ so, you'd rather be with your college friends then with us?

~ so, I guess you won't be hanging out with us after you graduate from college?

~ you'd rather study than hang out with us, whatever

and, in return, I never told them...

~ come on, you guys should go to college

~ what, are you guys going to work in a factory your whole lives?

~ don't you want to challenge yourself?

~ don't you want to provide for your family by having a better job?

Maybe we should've talked about me going to college and them not going to college? I don't know if it would've helped anyway, since it was never an issue—besides with Fred once in a while. I guess subconsciously we handled the whole situation the traditional Mexican way of dealing with issues—with *Denial Therapy*.

Denial Therapy is the preferred method of therapy for Mexicans. It's much better than Cognitive Behavioral Therapy or Psychoanalysis Therapy because it doesn't require seeing anyone with an advanced degree, there isn't a co-payment to make at the end of a session, the hours are flexible, and it's free.

Denial Therapy may not fix the issue at hand, but it makes the problem bearable for at least one more day.

"Whatever, dude. It's cool. I may not be able to make it either," Gilbert said.

"Just swing by the club after your class?" Alfonso suggested.

I ignored him, because I knew it'd be too late to drive all the way to Riverside after my class. A few minutes later, I left Tavo's Cave and headed back to Cal State Fullerton.

The elephant in the room turned out to be nothing more than a fly on the wall. I figured it wasn't going to be a big deal, even though, I must admit, for a second there I was a tad bit nervous about the issue.

My friends knew that I wasn't choosing college over them or anything like that. They knew that I was choosing "me" over everything—I was choosing "my" education and future.

The bottom line is that they never give me a hard time for going to college, and I never give them a hard time for not going to college—just as true friends should do to one another. They have my back, and I have theirs.

They did give me a hard time, though, when I didn't march after getting my A.A. degree from Fullerton College. I knew they were proud of me, and wanted to celebrate my accomplishment. However, I didn't participate in the graduation march because, to be honest, I didn't have a sense of accomplishment. My goal was to get a B.A., not just an A.A.

The Pittsburgh Steelers don't celebrate after finishing in first place during the regular season—they only celebrate after winning the Super Bowl. An A.A. degree was the regular season for me. I'm not going to pop the champagne cork until I win the Super Bowl—and that'll happen once I've completed all of the requirements needed for a Bachelor of Arts Degree in Liberal Studies from Cal State Fullerton.

SÍ 'CHE' PUEDE

When my cousin got married a few years ago, she and her husband chose an odd song for their first dance—*"Sí Nos Dejan."*

This means something like, "if they let us," we'll be together, is the implication.

The song is about a couple who want to be together, but apparently some people don't approve of their relationship. It has some nice lyrics, like -

Sí nos dejan ...

We'll love each other all of our lives

If they let us ...

We'll find a corner near heaven to live

The song sounds much better after a few beers. Hell, every Mexican song sounds better after a few beers. Mexican songs are like country songs, but with one big exception—Mexican songs are about being in love with girls, not with pick-up trucks or coonhounds.

The best Mexican composer and singer of all time is Jose Alfredo Jimenez. He's so loved in Mexico that there's a law requiring the police to arrest anybody being critical of him. Two-time offenders of the law are deported to El Salvador for a minimum of 2 years.

Vicente Fernandez has a much better voice than Jose Alfredo, but there's something about Jose Alfredo's voice that most Mexicans can relate to. I think it's because after a few drinks, we all think we can sing just like him. On the other hand, we all know, sober or drunk, we'll never come close to Chente's phenomenal voice.

As *Sí Nos Dejan* was being played, everybody was whispering to one another, "Who the hell is trying to stop them?" My uncle and aunt loved their new son-in-law, and my cousin's new in-laws loved her.

The song was an odd choice, but whatever—lots of couples still play the Village People's *"Y-M-C-A"* song at their wedding. Hell, my uncle has had it played at all three of his weddings—he just can't seem to let go of the '70s. That's why he's been divorced three times—he also can't stop using cocaine, listening to the Bee Gees, and he refuses to shave his sideburns.

My cousin's wedding immediately came to mind when I got back to the campus, because a protest was taking place, and I saw a poster that I equate with the *Sí Nos Dejan* song. High above the other signs, someone was carrying a bright yellow poster with bold black letters reading *Sí Se Puede*. Whenever I see this sign, I can't help but cringe.

Sí Nos Dejan and Sí Se Puede both seem too whiney to me.

There were some fifty students protesting in front of the administration building. I couldn't tell who they were or what the issue was about. The protest didn't look like a Mexican thing, an Asian thing, a Black thing, or a gabacho thing. Besides, I don't think gabachos are legally allowed to demand anything, anyway.

Suddenly, a group of them started chanting, "Sí se puede! Sí se puede!" as they marched up the stairs, leading to the entrance of the administration building. I didn't visually recognize anybody, but I sure as hell recognized one person's voice— Tina's. I knew she was in there somewhere because after the group would shout, "Sí se puede!" Tina could be heard yelling, "Órale!" It sounded funny.

"Sí se puede!"

"Órale!"

"Sí se puede!"

"Órale!"

"Sí se puede!"

"Órale!"

I guess I cringe when I hear Sí Se Puede, because I get the sense that the protesters chanting that phrase are like little kids who're being told by their parents that they can't do something, and the little kids, the protesters, are responding like little brats with, "Yeah we can, if we want to."

Parent: No you can't.

Protesters: Yes we can!

Parents: No you can't.

Protesters: Oh, yes we can!

Parents: No se puede.

Protesters: Sí se puede!

But the real issue I have with Sí Se Puede, and the reason I think it's "invisible" nowadays-is that I think the phrase has become obsolete after being used for so many years and for so many different causes.

Sí Se Puede chants are like car alarms going off in parking lots—we hear them so often, we don't even bother to turn around to see why they're going off. The car alarms and the chants are virtually synonymous.

"Sí se puede! Sí se puede!"

"Beep! Beep! Beep!"

"Sí se puede! Sí se puede!"

"Beep! Beep! Beep!"

"Sí se puede! Sí se puede!"

"Beep! Beep! Beep!"

And we all keep on walking past the car alarms, and past the issues at hand.

There're a lot of chants that bring about specific moments in history to mind:

~ No taxation, without representation

~ Remember the Alamo

~ Hell no, we won't go

These phrases had a specific time period and a specific issue they were addressing. When I see or hear Sí Se Puede, I think of *everything* under the sun and yet *nothing* at the same time. This is because the slogan has been beaten to death.

Its been used in everything from immigration rallies to high school pep-rallies to my aunt yelling enthusiastically at her 2-year-old son ...

~ *Sí se puede!*

~ *Sí se puede!*

... as he sat on the toilet trying to take a crap after being constipated for a couple of days.

Sí Se Puede has become a caricature of itself—it's now equivalent to the Mexican sleeping under the cactus with a big-ass sombrero and colorful poncho draped over his knees.

I think a lot of the unions, like the teachers' union and the state employees' union, have a special cash fund so there'll always be at least one person with a Sí Se Puede sign at every rally—it's an all-expenses-paid trip for the lowest-ranking union member forced to show up to the protest with the sign.

Last year I was in downtown Los Angeles trying to get some immigration paperwork taken care of at the Mexican Consulate when I ran into a rally protesting the death penalty. Some dude was finally going to get put to death after some 20 years on death row. There were all kinds of protest signs:

~ Two wrongs don't make a right

~ End the racist death penalty

~ The State isn't God

and

~ Sí se puede!

What the hell? In what crazy-ass context does that phrase even apply to the death penalty? Do they mean, "yes we can" kill him or "yes we can" save him?

Another time I was watching the news, and there was a "save the endangered bird" rally taking place in Nebraska, or Iowa. There were signs reading:

~ The world needs more birds, not another shopping center

~ Even China can't manufacture a *real* Whooping Crane

There were other signs as well, but in the middle of the crowd I saw some fool standing there with his Sí Se Puede sign.

I bet even the bird was confused with the sign—the poor bird probably thought the guy holding the sign was trying to get him accepted into an Ivy League University or some exclusive zoo.

I bet the damn bird didn't even read Spanish—he wasn't sure if the person with the sign wanted to shoot him or save him.

The protesters have to get rid of this generic slogan. It's as if the people protesting are too lazy to come up with something directed at the specific cause they're demonstrating for or against.

101

For example, if students want to protest the increase in tuition fees, they should get a poster that reads something like -

~ Higher tuition equals...

~ Less college graduates, equals...

~ More outsourcing to India, equals...

~ Higher unemployment!

~ Keep tuitions low, keep America strong!

I'm no marketing major, but I think this would get more people involved than a boring Sí Se Puede sign, because this appeals to the unemployed, the patriotic, and to those who don't give a crap about helping out the economy of third-world countries.

I know it's a long poster, but an arrow pointing up can replace the word "higher," and an arrow pointing down can replace the word "less." The word "equals" can even be replaced with "=".

Or this group can take the easy way out and make another Sí Se Puede sign.

I guess everyone recycles slogans. "Remember the Alamo" was used when American politicians wanted to get the people all riled up in the war against Mexico. Some 60 years later, "Remember the Maine" was used for the same purpose, except against Spain this time. But hell, at least 60 years had passed between the two slogans.

Speaking of rallies, the other thing I often see at Chicano rallies, which is extremely naive of them, are images of Che.

Che!?

Why him? Why are Chicanos holding up images and wearing t-shirts with Che on them? If they were true-blue Chicanos, and not sell-out Chicanos, they'd have people like Willie Velasquez, Modesta Avila, Emma Tenayuca, Edward

Roybal, Dolores Huerta, Corkey Gonzales, Reyes Lopes Tijerina, Sal Castro, or even bad-ass Fernando Valenzela on their protest posters, *but not Che*.

Tijerina, Reynoso, and others should be acknowledged for their hard work that went *directly towards improving the lives of Mexican-Americans in the United States, not an Argentine doctor that helped establish a brutal dictatorship in Cuba.*

Chicano activists keep complaining about being underrepresented in the school curriculum, and I agree with them 100%, but when they finally get a chance to "write the curriculum," they put an Argentine doctor on center stage?

What's with that?

They can't criticize "the man" when they're doing the same thing as "the man"—ignoring, us, themselves- *Mexicans*.

Is this because they're naive, or because they can't name any Mexican-American heroes? A little research can cure the latter issue, but first they have to become enlightened on the former issue. However, getting Chicano activists to accept this problem would be akin to someone going to therapy—the problem can be pointed out to them all day and night, but until they recognize the problem on their own, they'll deny and justify the whole issue, and continue doing whatever it is they shouldn't be doing—like alcoholics.

Che isn't seen at protest rallies in Mexico—only at Chicano rallies. That's because to Mexicans, Che isn't an iconic figure.

He might have started off as a revolutionary hero fighting against the corrupt Bautista government, but he blew his chance of being a true revolutionary hero because of the oppression and pain he inflicted on the Cuban people. He could have been a true revolutionary hero—a George Washington, a Lech Walesa, a David, a Nelson Mandela, or even an Emiliano Zapata, but he helped put Castro and communism in power. Nobody should ever be honored for placing a vicious and murderous government in power.

Mexicans in Mexico understand this. Mexicans know that if Che were alive today and president of a country, he'd put down any rally protesting his government—he'd even have his henchmen take the Sí Se Puede signs away from the Chicano protesters and have those signs shoved up their butts—that's what Che would do to the Chicano protesters.

Once in power, Che would be against any freedom of speech. Che would exile, jail, or kill anybody who would try expressing contrary opinions—because that's what takes place in Cuba, under the leadership of the man he helped place in power.

Fools with Che on their shirts might as well put on other images of corrupt and oppressive dictators: Idi Amin, Saddam Hussein, Pol Pot, Stalin, Pinochet, Franco, Porfirio Diaz, George Steinbrenner, or Al Davis.

To Chicano activists, Che is like the groom in an old wedding portrait. When people look back at the wedding, they remember the good times that took place *that night*—the laughter, the drinking, the dancing. That's how Chicanos look at Che.

What they don't see, what they don't want to remember, is all of the pain and suffering that the groom, Che, caused his family, Cuba, because of his abusive and oppressive ways of being—out of sight, out of mind. This is why ignorant Chicanos still embrace Che.

It's not right. It's not cool. It's not okay.

I walked past the protesters, avoiding the guys with clipboards that wanted people to sign the petition.

I got to class just as the professor was passing out the test. An hour later I walked out of there feeling pretty good about how I did. I think I nailed it with no less than a C-, and maybe even as high as a B, if the professor doesn't read the essay section; rumor has it he never reads the essay part of the test. I had no idea what the answer was to the question he asked, so I just summarized the Dodgers game from the night before. I wrote a lot and wrote pretty sloppily, hoping he'd assume that I must know the material.

A lot of people get nervous taking tests—not me. I'm one of the most consistent test takers I know. I've always been very confident in my ability to get a C on any test I take. If I take a hard test, I'll get a C on it. If I take an easy Spanish test, I'll also get a C. If I took an IQ test-I'd probably get a C on that thing, too.

The only problem I ever really had was in Mr. Keen's math classes, and the geometry class—and the astronomy and chemistry classes. Even then, I probably would've been able to pull off a C in those classes if I would've given a damn at the time. Well, maybe not in geometry; I just didn't get that stuff at all.

My overall grade point average in high school was a 2.65. At Fullerton College I excelled and pulled off a 2.85 GPA. Now, after a couple of years here at Cal State Fullerton, I regressed some—I'm currently around a 2.75 GPA.

I don't place too much of an emphasis on grades because I don't think they reflect one's intelligence, capabilities, or future success. I believe in a good GPA, but I don't believe in studying to the point of suicide in order to get those grades. I believe in doing a good job, but I'm not going to try and impress a professor with fancy words when I'm writing an essay. Who am I kidding? I couldn't use fancy words if I wanted to. My senior year in high school, I bought a book called *30 Days to a More Powerful Vocabulary*. I threw that pretentious book away after four pinche days.

This one girl I know, a psychology major, of course, said that I feel this way, regarding grades, because I have an insecurity complex—perhaps stemming from my childhood.

She said I must've felt some form of rejection from my parents—way wrong—or siblings—kind of right—and, therefore, I'm afraid of desiring anything because I may relive the sense of being rejected. She said that maybe as a child I went up to my father wanting a hug, but he gave me a handshake, instead.

She went on to theorize, supported by her fifteen units of upper division psychology classes, that I've developed a defensive mechanism that doesn't allow me to desire anything, or to put my whole heart and energy into anything, because that way if I don't get the desired hug, in other words, the desired grade, I won't feel a sense of rejection.

She said that to me, subconsciously, the professors are playing the role of my father, and I'm too afraid to ask them for a "hug," meaning I'm too afraid to give my best effort on a test because I may receive a low grade, and I would internalize that low grade as the handshake my father gave me when I was a child, thus experiencing once again the painful sense of rejection.

Finally, psycho-girl went on to say that I most likely apply this same defensive mechanism in relationships. She said that I probably don't ask out the girls I'd like to ask out because I'm afraid of being rejected by them. And as long as I don't ask those girls out, I can't get rejected by them—like, as long as I don't put my hand in the fire, I won't get burned.

I think she included this psychobabble crap because she wanted me to ask her out. She gave me a *kind of a look*, as if saying, "Ask me out, and I'll give you a hug, not a handshake."

Even though I hadn't had a date in a long time, *a very long time*, I wasn't about to ask her out. Everyone knows the most screwed-up students on campus are the psychology majors. They go into this field because they want to know why their own lives are so messed up. And after they think they've dealt with their childhood issues, issues they'll probably repeat with their own children, they then spend the rest of their lives bugging the crap out of people by trying to psychoanalyze them.

If she was a sociology major, I would've asked her out, though. Sociology majors believe it's society that's messed-up, not them. They also don't seem to have "father issues" that they take out on their boyfriends like the psychology girls do.

I ignored her comment by pretending I had something in my eye. It's a childish move, but effective—that's why kids do it all the time. I then proceeded to explain to her why her theory about me was wrong. I started by telling her that I've gotten roughly seven As throughout my entire academic career, therefore proving I wasn't afraid to "give it my all," despite the possibility of being "rejected."

I also told her that I have gone after girls—well, *a girl*, I was interested in; I asked Mary Dalton to the Disco-mania dance in eighth grade. I must admit, though, I was nervous as hell when I asked her out because the odds weren't in my favor—she was white, rich, blond, A.S.B. Vice-President, and a Jehovah's Witness. I just couldn't picture Mary going up to her mother and asking-

"Mom, I was asked to the Disco-Mania Dance. Can I go?"

"Who asked you?"

"Hector."

"Hector? Is he Greek?"

"Zamora."

"Oh."

"Mexican—I think. Or maybe he's from *Guadalajara*."

"Where does he live?"

"I don't know. Some apartments near Blake Field, I guess."

"What Kingdom Hall does he attend?"

"He doesn't. He's Catholic."

"Oh, okay. Have fun with Hector at the Disco-Mania Dance—the Mexican, possibly *Guadalajaran* Catholic whose family can't afford a house."

The conversation must've gone something like that, because she did go to the dance with me. My parents made me take her a red corsage on the night of the dance, and to her parents I took a block of cheese—the government's finest. It was embarrassing as hell because I wanted to take her a white corsage, not a red one.

As I was telling this story to psycho-girl, she got up without saying a word and left. I don't know if she left to take her meds, if she was no longer interested in me, if she was upset because she realized all of those upper division units she took in psychology didn't apply to the real world, or what.

What I do know, however, was that her theories about me were wrong, sort of. She was a little right and a little wrong, as I came to find out later.

HEEECCCTTTOOORRR

I headed towards the pub because I knew it was comedy night.

Every other month stand-up comedians perform at the pub. Some of them are great, and others suck big time. After the comedians perform, they open it up to the audience. Anyone can give it a shot as a stand-up comic.

For years I've had a deep-down secret desire to give it a try, but I've chickened out every time—maybe I should look around for a *Become a Stand-Up Comic* brochure?

Sometimes I don't have the courage to get up and go on stage; other times I convince myself that I have other, more important things to do. The thought of a microphone being the only thing separating me from the audience petrifies me.

The pub was already crowded. I found a little table in the back and ordered some nachos and a Coke. The show wasn't going to start for another hour, so I ate as fast as I could to give myself an excuse to leave-if I was done eating and the show hadn't started, I figured I could chalk it up as having given it a try.

I was scraping up the last of the melted cheese from the bottom of my nachos plate when Nick, my long-lost friend, walked in.

Nick spoke fluent Spanish—therefore, somewhat by default, he was majoring in Spanish. He could've majored in any subject he wanted to—he's very smart. However, he knew if he went pre-med or was interested in becoming an engineer, he'd have to put some serious time into his studies. To his credit, he was smart enough *not* to fool himself into thinking his natural intelligence would carry him through the rigors of those academic fields.

Nick ordered us a pitcher of beer and a basket of hot wings. Before I knew it, we were on our second pitcher of beer, and the show had started.

The first two comedians were funny as hell, but the third one was awful. All of his jokes started off with, "Oh, so the other day..." A few people started heckling him. At the end of his routine, though, the audience gave him a decent round of applause—for effort, I guess. The host of the show then got up on stage and confronted those that had given the comic a hard time.

"If you think this is so easy, then get your ass up here and try it. I bet none of you could last 2 minutes up here," he challenged the hecklers. Just then, one of the hecklers stood up and walked onto the small stage.

"What's your name, smart-ass," the host asked the heckler.

"Bob. Bob...uh...Wood...*Woodward*," he responded. A few people snickered.

"You had to think about it? Dude, you're attending a university, not a community college." A lot of people laughed. I don't know if they laughed because the host didn't get the "Bob Woodward" joke, or if their laughter was directed towards the "community college" part. Just in case, neither Nick nor I laughed. Hell, Nick was even wearing a Fullerton College t-shirt. I don't know why they laughed, though—it's not like these fools were attending Berkeley or UCLA.

"Bob Woodward" turned out to be pretty funny. The guy running the show was even impressed. It turned out that "Bob" was a political science major, which was why he made a lot of political jokes. They say that's the key to being funny—talk about what you know.

"Does anybody else want to give it a try?" the host asked. Nobody moved a muscle. "Come on, don't be afraid. Look how good it turned out for our community college transfer student."

The host walked around the pub holding the microphone out to see if he had any takers. Nobody stepped up. Then Nietzsche came to mind: live dangerously, he once wrote. After drinking the two pitchers of beer, I was now willing to do just that—well, at least I was willing to give it some serious thought.

Nick must have sensed that I was tempted to grab the microphone from the guy because he said, "Don't think about it, just do it." So I did. I raised my hand and waited to be called on.

"Come on down here, fool, nobody can see you from way back there," the host said, as he motioned me towards him. The walk down to the stage was agonizing. I've never been executed before, but I now know how it must feel to walk to the execution room. The thought even occurred to me that those on death row should just be shot in their prison cells, instead of having them make the torturous walk to the execution room. But then I thought, screw them, they should have to walk to the execution room—they've been convicted of first-degree murder. The only "crime" I've committed, though, is thinking that I have something funny to say.

What seemed like a half-hour later, I finally made it to the stage.

"What's your name?" the host asked me.

"Hector".

"Hector? *So, that's a real name, huh?* Hector what?"

"Zamora"

"Here he is, *a good friend of mine, Hector Zamora*. Give it up for-*Heeeccctttooorrr*," the host yelled out as he walked off the stage, handing me the microphone.

111

I looked into the audience, but I couldn't see a thing. The people up close seemed blurry, and past them it was total darkness. I didn't know when to start my routine, either—I couldn't tell if the people were still clapping or if they had stopped. Hell, I couldn't tell if they had ever clapped at all.

My whole body and mind went numb. I had no idea what to do next. Then, in a flash, I remembered something from a speech class I took a long time ago. My professor, Mr. Phelan, taught us that it's very important to get comfortable with one's physical surroundings when delivering a speech. Therefore, he told us to move things around—to control our environment. By doing this, he explained, we're demonstrating a sense of confidence. In addition, it gives us a second or two to settle down and catch our breath.

I had no idea how long I had been standing there, so I thought that maybe I should just get right into the routine. But, luckily for me, speech was one of the few classes I did manage to get an A in. So I took a step back and followed Mr. Phelan's recommendations—I moved the stool over 2 feet, then I moved the microphone stand up about a foot, next I picked up the glass of water the last comic had left on the small stage and placed it on the nearest table—then I thought about getting the hell out of there.

As I was about to take my first step towards the exit door, psycho-girl came to mind. She was right, in this case-I was scared of being rejected. I've always been the funny guy in the group—from kindergarten to now. But *these people* don't know that—they don't know that what I usually have to say is funny, at least to me. I don't have a proven track record with them. To them I'm just a stranger, a faceless stranger that they'll forget ever existed a minute after I leave the stage.

I took a deep breath and tied my shoelaces. I knew it was time to confront the possibility that I may not be as funny as I think I am.

Maybe it won't be so bad? I've always heard that the fear of flying is worse than the actual flight. So with that in mind, I took a deep breath, and went for it ...

Thank you, thank you, please have a seat.

My name is Hector Zamora. I'm light, but not white. To be honest, it sucks knowing that other people don't see me as something that I am: a Mexican.

It looks like some of you Mexicans out there don't have anything to worry about—you got "I'm a wetback" written all over you. Some of you look like you even got a D- in your ESL classes. Lucky bastards.

I hate *not* being recognized as a Mexican by others. It's made my life hard, sometimes. Like in elementary school, I always got in arguments with the lunch lady because she didn't believe that I was Mexican, so she wouldn't give me my free lunch.

I just got back from Mexico. I visited the pyramids and the cenotes. *Cenotes*, fools, not *cerotes* —cochinos.

If you ever go climbing pyramids in Mexico, I suggest you take your own first-aid kit because they don't have any of that stuff

113

down there. This kid fell down some 30 feet on a pyramid, and his frantic mother asked the tour guide for a first-aid kit. He tossed her a "Mexican First Aid Kit"—a rosary, a picture of Jesus, some Holy Water, and an orange Fanta—in a plastic bag with a popote (straw).

My cousin from Mexico, Paola, is all into labels and fashion. She loves being *trendy*. So, you know how everyone is naming their kids Paris, London, Sydney, and names like that? You know, after fashionable cities. Well, she wants to be trendy, but she also wants her kids to never forget that they're Mexican, so she named her son D.F. and her daughter Sinaloa. She's pregnant, and said if it's a girl, she'll name her Tijuana, and if it's a boy, Durango.

I think it's interesting how she's all trendy, but her brother is so down to earth. She stayed in Mexico, while he came up to el norte. I hadn't seen him in a while, so I went to his work the other day at Home Depot. Well, he doesn't *technically* work for Home Depot, he's more of an independent contractor who works just outside of Home

Depot—on the sidewalk—waiting for a ride to work—by whoever picks him up.

When I was at Home Depot looking for my cousin, I ran into someone I knew from high school. Fidel was his name. He was *all Chicano* and down with *la raza*. But he told me he now works for the County of Los Angeles as a dogcatcher. I'm like, what happened? You were all about helping your people and community, now you're a dogcatcher? Yeah, he said, I am still helping out my community—rabies are down 34% in the barrios I patrol, fool! And last month I set a county record for most pit bulls and Chihuahuas caught in a calendar month.

Has anyone taken a shot of tequila tonight? Speaking of shots, my cousin never gave her twin daughters their immunization shots because she's afraid they may become autistic because of the mercury in the shots, and she's very concerned about their health. *Yet,* she has no problem giving her kids churros for breakfast. They're not autistic, but they're a couple of fat-ass 4 year olds with type 2 diabetes.

Thank you, good night. I'm done.

I placed the microphone on the stool and walked back to my table. I didn't know if the people were applauding or not. I was a bundle of nerves, oblivious to every sight and sound around me.

I sat down in my chair, and Nick gave me a slap on the back. I didn't know if it was a "good job" slap or if it was a "nice try" slap.

I downed the rest of my beer as Nick talked to me. I had no idea what he was saying to me—I just kept bobbing my head up and down, like my mother's comadres. Someone walked by me and also gave me a slap on the back. Damn it! I thought to myself—what are they trying to tell me with those slaps?

I was cursing the day I heard Nietzsche's "live dangerously" advice. Maybe Nietzsche meant to live dangerously by being a cholo and driving around in an ugly-ass Honda Accord, not by trying to be a stand-up comic?

The host was saying something to me, but I couldn't understand him—I was experiencing post-traumatic stress, I think. To me, he sounded like Charlie Brown's dad—all I heard was, "*Wa –wawa-wa.*"

We walked out of the pub pretty hammered. I knew I wasn't in any condition to drive, so I didn't—I let Nick drive me home. I've never figured out why drunks who know they're too drunk to drive themselves home think it's okay to let their drunk-ass friends drive them home.

Luckily, we got home safe that night. I think we hit a cat on La Habra Boulevard, but that's just a guess—it could've been a raccoon.

As I went to bed, I was feeling proud of myself for having done something I've been wanting to do for a long time. But the messed-up part was that I still didn't know if I had done a good or a bad job. I didn't ask Nick about it after we left the pub, and he didn't bring it up, either. I was also thinking that I wouldn't have minded hearing a "Sí se puede!" at the pub that night. Hell, I would've been happy with an "Órale!" from Tina.

The next day my brother Alvaro drove me to school. I told him my car battery had died and that a friend would give me a jump later. I told him that nobody had cables last night—that's why I had to get a ride home.

He dropped me off at the front of the university. I was walking to my first class when I saw Jinsoo sitting on a bench. I opened up a book to pretend I was reading so I wouldn't have to talk to his ass. My plan worked—I didn't talk to him; he just talked to me.

"So which painting did you decide to enter?" he asked me as I kept my head down. I just shrugged my shoulders and kept walking. Thank God I walked by el chino, though—I had forgotten about the application. I still wasn't sure which painting to enter, and time was winding down.

I wanted to go in search of Dr. Padilla, but I had to get to my history class. We were having a test next week, and I couldn't afford to miss another lecture. That's the problem with being a solid C student—there's very little wiggle room to play around with. Students with As or solid Bs can afford to miss a class or two. Not C students—we're always just one missed lecture away from dropping down to a D.

"A" students can afford to miss a class, not only because they have good grades, but because they'll borrow the notes from up to five different people to get the information they missed. Not us C students. When we miss a lecture, we just assume the information we missed won't be on the test coming up, so we don't ask to borrow anyone's notes.

Dr. Padilla's office was in the next building over from my class. I decided I'd go by there after my history class.

117

HE'S A SHE

I was sitting on the floor outside of Dr. Padilla's office with my legs stretched out and my eyes closed, when I heard the sexy sound of heels coming my way from down the hall.

I was going to open my eyes with the anticipation that it'd be a voluptuous coed coming my way to introduce herself to me, but I knew that the odds of that actually happening were *zero*. So I just kept my eyes shut, assuming the heels belonged to a secretary on her way to the copy machine.

When the "secretary" got close to me, I pulled my legs in so she wouldn't trip over them. The trotting heels stopped right in front of me, and the "secretary" asked me, "Can I help you?"

I opened my eyes and was going to tell her that I was just waiting for Dr. Padilla to show up for his office hours. The lady looked like Mrs. Brady from the *Brady Bunch,* except with shorter hair and a few years older. She was carrying some books and what looked like a stack of student research papers.

I was about to discover that she wasn't someone's secretary; rather, *she was Dr. Padilla*. It took some impressive reasoning skills on my part to arrive at that conclusion.

My first clue was, why would she ask if she could help me when I was sitting in front of Dr. Padilla's office? Obviously the only person who'd be able to help me, would be Dr. Padilla.

The next clue came in the form of the nametag she was wearing. It read *Professor C. Padilla, Art Department.*

"I, um, just had a few questions about the art contest," I finally blurted out.

119

"Sure, come on in my office and we'll get those questions answered for you," she said, unlocking the door and letting us both in.

I was feeling pretty stupid – all along I had assumed that Dr. Padilla was a man. In Mexico I would've know she was a woman because her name in the class schedule would've read "Profesora," with an "a' at the end, indicating a female. But in the United States, the word "professor" applies to both sexes.

I think all professors should go by their first names, then just initial their last names; that way there won't be any surprises, unless Dr. Padilla had a first name like my middle name— Guadalupe. In that case, I still wouldn't have been able to tell one way or the other if Guadalupe was a male or female.

I think my middle name is emasculating. Or de-masculating? Whichever word is the one that describes me feeling like I'm having my balls cut off whenever someone calls me *Guadalupe* – that's the word I'm looking for.

So there I was, at last, in the office containing the vital information needed to determine which painting I should enter. I sat down on a very uncomfortable antique chair. I think she purposely put that there so students like me won't stay long.

Once again, I used my brilliant reasoning skills to analyze the stuff in the room. After a few seconds of processing the information, I came to the conclusion that Dr. Padilla wasn't a white Mexican; rather, she is a white lady who married a man with a Spanish surname—mostly likely, by playing the odds, a fellow Mexicano.

I reached this conclusion because there wasn't a single Frida Kahlo painting hanging on the wall—and everyone knows that all educated Latinas are obligated to have at least one Frida painting hanging on their wall, or, at the very least-a Frida biography in their bookshelves.

Latinas with Frida paintings on their walls are also sending out a subliminal message to any potential male suitor that pretty much says: *I don't need you in my life to value myself. I won't take any crap from you. You either see me as your equal, or get lost.*

The painting's message itself is subliminal, but the ladies with Frida paintings on their walls aren't so subtle—they'll vocalize the subliminal message, loud and clear, in a heartbeat.

Dr. Padilla had an eclectic collection of paintings around her office. There was a Raphael, a Goya, and a Lichtenstein. They obviously weren't originals, but they did have nice wooden frames. What an odd collection, I thought to myself. I couldn't remember the names of any of the paintings, though. I'm sure an A student would've memorized the names and even the years they were painted—those minions will memorize just about anything for an A.

"So, how can I help you?" Dr. Padilla asked me, snapping me out of my investigation.

"Well, the title of the contest is 'Our Community.' Exactly what community is the committee interested in capturing?" I knew she didn't understand what I was saying—I realized this because of her question.

"What do you mean?"

I wasn't sure how to follow this up. I didn't think it was necessary to ask any more questions—I had gathered all of the information needed to realize that I should enter the *Self* painting if I wanted a shot at the thousand bucks.

This lady obviously wasn't interest in *Flying Blue Taco* themes; otherwise she'd have a Frida painting on her wall, or at the very least, a Carmen Garza painting. Now I just needed to figure out a way to get the hell out of her office without looking like an idiot.

"I mean, is there a specific aspect of the community that you and the committee are interested in capturing? Is it the physical, psychological, cultural, or metaphysical attributes that I should be focusing on?"

I don't even know what the hell "metaphysical" even means, but it did sound pretty deep, I thought.

"Actually, the whole point is to see what you guys create; to see what you guys have to say. We want to see how this generation views and interprets your own communities."

I was about to thank her and leave, when I noticed something that shook me to the core. Shivers went from my ass all the way up to my brain. On her keychain, sitting on the desk, was a miniature painting by Frida—*The Broken Column*.

What the hell? I thought to myself, who is this lady?

Is she a white Mexican or a white lady married to a Mexican?

Maybe I should enter the *Flying Blue Tacos* painting, instead?

I then decided if I can't figure out who she is, I probably won't guess right on which painting to enter into the art contest-so I decided to let her in on my dumb-ass plan.

"Well, the thing is, I have two paintings and I can't decide which one to enter." I then proceeded to explain to her my *Flying Blue Tacos* and *Self* theories.

She didn't say a word the whole time—I couldn't tell if she was mesmerized or bored. When I was done with my explanations, she asked me which painting I liked better.

"Whichever one gives me the best shot at winning the thousand bucks," I responded. My response sounded wrong the instant I finished saying it. It reminded me of the time I told the guy interviewing me for a shipping and receiving position at Sears, after he had just pretty much told me that I was hired, "But I need 2 weeks off in August because my cousin is getting married in Mexico, and I'm in the wedding."

The guy never ended up offering me the job, and I never ended up attending my cousin's fictional wedding in Mexico.

The way I had described it, it kind of made me sad that it never actually happened. I told the guy the wedding was going to be held at a luxurious hacienda, two mariachi groups would be playing, a fireworks show was going to take place at midnight, and a special bullfight session was going to take place because my cousin was marrying a bull fighter—I missed out on a good time.

Mexicans, like myself, tend to have a knee-jerk reaction whenever we get hired, or think we're about to be hired—we instinctively throw in the, "my cousin is getting married in Mexico" scenario and ask for some time off. Maybe I should've just asked him for 1 week off, instead of 2?

"Well, if it doesn't matter to you which painting you turn in, why don't you turn in the one you can relate to the most?" Dr. Padilla suggested. She then turned into a damn therapist—she leaned in towards me, and, in a soft tone of voice asked, "Are you, yourself, a *Blue Taco* or a *Self?*"

Oh, crap-that's not what I came here for. I came to get answers from the "horse's mouth," not to seek out some kind of spiritual awareness regarding my identity! I can't even answer which painting I like better; now she wants me to pick the painting I identify with the most? Come on, lady!

It's not like I consciously painted the paintings with the meanings I've attached to them. I first painted them while I was daydreaming of a bunch of other crap, and then later on I attached some symbolism specifically for this contest.

I could've painted a banana and somehow related it to the "Our Community" contest with some bullshit meaning.

> The banana is protected by a hard exterior, which symbolizes the macho nature of Mexican-Americans. However, once one peels off the protective shell of the Mexican-American, there's nothing but a soft, warm, soulful person inside.

In addition, bananas come in
bunches. This is also indicative of
a Mexican-American family—we
are close, loving, and often live
in large groups.

I really don't care about my paintings—I'm not an artist. I'm
just a poor college student trying to complete a required class
and win some money along the way.

"One never knows," Dr. Padilla said, "perhaps the voice of
your generation will emerge from this contest? And, perhaps,
you can be that voice?"

Seriously? The voice of my generation? Give me a break! I
have no idea what the hell this generation has to say. Besides, if
my generation does want something, it certainly isn't demanding
it.

I started feeling a little stressed out. Last night I was hanging
out at the pub drinking beer with Nick. Now, some 12 hours
later, I'm being asked to identify myself as a *Blue Taco* or a *Self-*
and being told that my paintings could possibly be the voice of
my generation?

Just as I was thinking about how crazy life can change in 12
hours, it hit me—Dr. Padilla was just messing around with me.
She had me going for a minute, but I finally got the joke.

Like the time I thought I won $5,000 from a lottery scratcher
ticket on my birthday. After jumping up and down and yelling,
"*Who's the man? Who's the man?*" for 5 minutes straight, I
eventually realized the joke was on me—it was a bogus ticket
my sister had bought at the liquor store for 10 bucks.

Right away, I felt better realizing that Dr. Padilla was
messing around with me. I thanked her for her time and left. As I
was walking down the hall, I realized that I should've taken a
look at her wedding finger to see if she was married or not. I
guess I'd have to find out some other time if she was a white
Mexican or a white lady married to a Mexican.

As I walked down the hall, I couldn't help but laugh to myself thinking that she thought I might be the voice of my generation—that was a good one. I couldn't wait to tell them back at Tavo's Cave about what had just happened. I knew they'd all get a good laugh out of this, especially Fred.

THE QUANTUM LIST

I went to the study room in the library to hang out, but nobody was there—not Lourdes, el chino, Paul, or anybody else.

So I studied for a while, then I took a break. I killed some time by looking at some magazines, then by listening to some science nerd talking about quantum physics.

Actually, I'm not sure if he was talking to me or talking to himself out loud—I was waiting for the elevator when he walked up to me and started yapping away. After listening to him for a few minutes, I excused myself and walked away. I felt kind of rude doing that, but I don't think he even noticed I had left.

I headed back to the study room hoping somebody would've shown up by now, but nobody had.

I didn't feel like studying anymore, nor did I feel like going home— just the thought of walking to my car tired me out. I was leaning back in the chair with my feet on the table, not thinking of anything in particular, when Mrs. Barcher, my third-grade teacher, suddenly came to mind.

Mrs. Barcher always had us making a "pros and cons" list to help us become better decision makers. Every Monday she'd write a topic on the chalkboard, and we'd write the pros and cons that would result from our actions, such as -

~ What will happen if I don't do my homework tonight?

~ What will happen if I cut in front of others in the lunch line?

~ What will happen if I share with others?

~ What will happen if I help someone understand their homework?

Although we all thought this exercise was stupid and boring at the time, it actually still comes to mind once in a while whenever I have to make a decision—it even saved my life once back in high school.

We were all partying at Steve Camacho's house before the football game against Sonora. Gilbert was driving that night, and he was drunk off his butt when he told me that he was taking off to go to some huge party in Whittier where there'd be lots of girls, and asked if I wanted to go with him.

I knew Gilbert was drunk, so Mrs. Barcher's pros and cons exercise went through my mind.

On the con side, I thought, we can get in an accident and die. However, on the pro side–there were a lot of girls at the party in Whittier.

Apparently the slightest possibility of hooking up with a girl outweighed the possibility of crashing into a telephone pole and dying, so I got in Gilbert's car, buckled up, and headed to the party in Whittier.

Ten minutes after we left, the cops busted Steve Camacho's party and took everybody to the police station. Nobody was allowed to leave until a parent picked them up.

If I would've stayed at the party, and if my dad would've picked me up at the police station-he would've killed me before ever leaving the parking lot.

I realize it wasn't the decision Mrs. Barcher would've liked for me to have made, but it worked out pretty good for me that night—even though, as it turned out, there weren't any girls at the party in Whittier like Gilbert had said there would be.

I guess Mrs. Barcher's exercise came to mind because the question Dr. Padilla had asked me earlier was still on my mind:

Mrs. Barcher's simple exercise seemed like the perfect way to go about answering this question—I needed to make a list.

So, with a third-grade decision making exercise in mind, I pulled out two pieces of paper. Instead of writing "pros" on top of one of the papers, I wrote, *Why I'm a Taco.* On the other paper I wrote, *Why I'm a Self.*

I thought I'd be able to fill in the sections quickly, but I just ended up staring at the papers for a while.

Deep in my heart, though, I knew I wanted to fill up the Taco section more—I wanted to be a Taco. I felt like a Taco, too, a proud-ass carne asada Taco soaked with chile verde, but I knew I had one big problem—the world doesn't see me as a Taco, the world sees me as a hamburger, a *Self.* I have salsa in my veins, but ketchup on my face.

Hell, not only does the world see me as a hamburger, my own siblings used to tell me I was a hamburger when I was a kid. My two brothers and sister are darker than me, so they'd always tell me that I was adopted—except they didn't put it as nicely as just saying, "You're adopted." They had harsher words to let me know I wasn't one of them.

"You're not our real brother, *we found you at the park.*"

"You're not one of us, *that's why you're so white.*"

"Your real mom abandoned you, just like the dogs at the pound. *We rescued you.*"

It was during these verbal attacks that I missed my oldest sister the most, even though I've never met her, nor will I ever meet her—in this world, at least. She was my mom and dad's first born, but unfortunately she passed away 2 weeks after blowing out the candles on her first birthday cake—an incompetent nurse screwed up the medications she was giving my sister for some internal infection she had, and this eventually led to her body shutting down and then dying.

She died 5 years before I was born, yet I miss her as if she were part of my everyday life—because to me, she has been.

I miss her because her skin complexion was as light as mine; therefore, we would've been a team. The way I always imagined it was that she'd hear my brothers and sister making fun of me, when suddenly, out of nowhere, she'd appear in the room, like a superhero, ready to rescue me from the heartless villagers and their flaming torches.

After fighting them off, she'd turn and give me a huge hug, and I wouldn't feel alone anymore—I'd know I had someone on my side.

"Don't listen to them," she'd tell me, "after all, you have me."

And although I never got a hug from her, just knowing that she would've given me the biggest hug in the world made me feel better—it comforted me. There was never a doubt in my mind that she was, and continues to be, my guardian angel.

Maybe psycho-girl was right about the whole rejection crap and all, but it was my siblings' acceptance that I was after, not my dad's.

Anyway, my two brothers and sister didn't really have a right to talk crap to me—it's not like they have the prototypical, stereotypical Mexican look, either. They all could've easily been adopted by an Iranian family as kids, been raised in Tehran, and nobody would ever have suspected a thing because a lot of Iranians and Mexicans look alike—every Mexican family has an uncle named Juan Jose Juarez who can pass as Akbar Amin Ashar.

My two brothers have been called Camel Jockeys on several occasions, and my sister hates getting gas on the corner of Imperial and Walnut because the attendant, some Iranian guy, keeps hitting on her because he thinks she's Persian—he refuses to believe she's Mexican, even though she has cussed him out in Spanish several times. As far as he's concerned, though, the fact that she can say, *"Eres un pendejo" (You're an idiot)* doesn't impress him because even old white ladies from La Habra have yelled that in Spanish at him.

It took me a while, but I finally realized that the "odd sibling out" gets picked on—it's just part of the dynamics that siblings go through, I guess. I have a tall cousin who's always getting picked on by his shorter sisters. Two brothers with huge acne problems who live in the back of the apartment complex always used to make fun of their brother with smooth skin—as soon as he got some pimples, they stopped picking on him. I've done my share of name-calling, also.

I called Sophia, "pimple-face."

Alvaro, "four-eyes."

Santiago, "fat-ass."

Eventually, however, Sophia's pimples went away, Alvaro got contacts, Santiago got so fat I felt bad making fun of him, and I finally believed my mother that I wasn't adopted.

While growing up, my mother always assured me that I wasn't adopted. I would've preferred she beat the crap out of my brothers and sister whenever they'd tell me I was adopted than to have her reassurance, though. After a few ass-whippings, I'm sure they would've stopped telling me such awful things.

She once told me that on the day I was born, I was the only baby in the small hospital in Jalos; therefore, it was impossible to mix me up with another baby. However, she'd proceed to thank God that I was born in Mexico, because if I had been born in the United States, she would've always wondered if I was her child—she says she would've wondered if I had been mixed up with an "American" baby back at the nursery by some china nurse.

I guess I never let the fact that they'd tell me I was adopted get to me too much, because I knew they loved me despite what they'd say. Sure, it hurt, but not to the point where I wanted to commit suicide or anything like that. If anything, I would've murdered them before killing myself.

131

So with a little hesitation, I grabbed the Taco paper and started writing reasons as to why I'm a Taco.

WHY I'M A TACO

~ When my parents would take us to the snow as kids, we had to use plastic bags from the supermarket for "snow boots." We double-bagged our sneakers whenever we'd go in the deep snow.

~ I've been working on my citizenship application for 7 years.

~ In high school, I always voted for the Mexican running for anything, like A.S.B. or Homecoming Queen. The only exception is when I voted for Jessica Salazar for tenth-grade Treasurer—turned out, she was Filipina.

~ I share a bedroom with two brothers—and any male visiting relative.

~ I've never believed in Santa Claus. My parents made it a point to let us know that it's *el niñito Jesús*, Baby Jesus, that brought us our gifts. I remember wondering to myself, when I was about 9 years old, after opening up my only gift, "Why is Baby Jesus so cheap?"

~ My car has three different shades of blue.

~ I'm not a math or science major.

~ One of my fondest childhood memories was listening to Jaime Jarrin announcing the Dodgers games while sitting on the couch with my father.

~ I was always Mil Máscaras, El Blue Demon, or El Santo when wrestling against my friends.

~ I always wanted the Indians to kill the cowboys on the television shows I'd watch—I thought John Wayne was the devil himself.

132

~ At night it was, and continues to be, la Llorona or el Cucuy outside of my window making noises-not the Boogie Man

~ I can eat 10 mazapans without getting sick

~ A family day out meant a trip to the swap meet.

~ As a kid, I thought Mighty Mouse was Mexican-and I still think he might be.

I couldn't think of any more examples for my list. I bet if I asked the fools back at Tavo's Cave for more examples, they'd give me thousands of things to add to the list, starting with, "You have a Green Card, fool. Enough said."

Next was coming up with examples I really didn't want to admit to, because my illegal cousins here would then say something like, "*Hombre*, you might as well turn in your Green Card for a citizenship certificate, because if these things are true, you've already crossed to the other side."

WHY I'M A SELF

~ My favorite band is Led Zeppelin.

~ I don't watch Univision or Telemundo.

~ I've heard of *Tin Tan*, but I don't know if it's a dog, a person, or the title of a famous Mexican movie.

~ None of my radio buttons are set to Spanish stations.

~ I prefer flour tortillas over corn tortillas.

~ I've never been placed in a bilingual class.

~ Our television, stove, and kitchen cabinets have all their knobs.

~ I have car insurance—just collision, not comprehensive, of course.

~ Our couches aren't covered with plastic—anymore.

~ I've never been a *chambelán* in a cousin's quinceañera.

~ I'd rather watch the Super Bowl than the World Cup final.

~ I've never taken a burrito to school for lunch.

~ I can't name any Mexican president besides Benito Juarez.

~ I know what the Dow Jones is.

~ I don't have a cousin living within a 5-mile radius of our apartment.

~ I'd rather drink Corona than Budweiser.

~ I think jalapeños *are* hot.

~ I've never flown out of or landed in the Tijuana airport.

I stared at the list for a while. I just looked at it, wondering to myself what was the point of making this list. Nobody is exclusively a Taco or a Self. I have a cousin named Johnny who doesn't speak a word of Spanish, yet he has the Mexican flag across the dashboard of his car, eats jalapeños by the handful, and loves menudo—so is he a Taco or a Self?

I know a guy who grew up in Oaxaca, but is now an American citizen majoring in biology, and he hates Vicente Fernandez and lucha libre—is he a Taco or a Self?

And then it hit me—I suddenly understood what the science nerd at the elevator was talking about. The quantum physics stuff he was yapping away about applies to the lists I made, and my paintings.

From what I remember, he said that Einstein was a fool because in Einstein's world, everything is orderly, predictable, and certain—as if a five-star general was in charge of running the world. Therefore, in his world, if I wore plastic bags as snow boots, according to my list, I'm a *Taco*. Likewise, since Led Zeppelin is my favorite band, I'm a *Self*.

Well, this order and predictability breaks down if I were to walk through the snow wearing plastic bags as snow boots, being a Taco, while at the same time listening to Led Zeppelin, being a Self. The obvious question is, at that moment, am I a Taco or a Self? In Einstein's world I have to be one or the other, like an element on the periodic table, I guess.

The nerd then talked about quantum physics. In the quantum world, the world is very weird—beyond weird. In this world, apparently, a single object can be in many different places at the same time—an object can be here, there, and in ten other places simultaneously, if not more. I think hippies on acid are running this world.

So therefore, from what I understand, the way I see it, what I make of it, what I think the nerd on medication was saying, is that if I were able to step into the world of quantum physics, I can be a *Taco* and a *Self* concurrently—I don't have to be exclusively one or the other.

I really liked the idea that I can have one foot in each of the paintings, so to speak—that I can be a Taco while at the same time being a Self, and a Self while at the same time being a Taco. And this wasn't just some bullshit realization I made; this stuff is backed up by science! Who would've thought that quantum physics would help put me at ease with my identity crisis?

I love being a Taco because I love being Mexican, and all that comes with it. But I also love being a Self because I don't feel so limited, so restricted by the cultural norms, even though they're mostly self-imposed.

After this realization, I wasn't quite sure what to do with my paintings. I still wanted to enter the contest, but I wasn't sure which one to submit—I hadn't gotten any closer to figuring out which one to turn in despite having had my conversation with Dr. Padilla.

I thought of just changing the title of one paining to *Chingon (Badass)* and the other one to *Muy Chingon (A Big Badass)*. This would make it very easy for me to decide which one I should enter in the contest—*Muy Chingon*, of course.

I crumbled up the lists and headed to my car.

ADD—GOD'S NATURAL ENERGY DRINK

I decided to turn in *Flying Blue Tacos*.

As it turned out, though, even if I would've turned in *Self*, it wouldn't have made a difference—neither one of them had a chance in hell of winning.

The contest had achieved its goal—there were some very cool paintings entered by Mexican-American, non-art majors. I guess all those years of spray painting graffiti in alleys and doodling on their Pee-Chee folders during class finally paid off for some of them.

"Quality" sure turned out being the operative word in the contest. I guess I was doomed from the start—I didn't have much quality in either of my paintings. All of my time strategizing didn't pay off one bit. Apparently, bullshitting some symbolism behind a painting can get me a grade in class, but that stuff doesn't fly in the real world.

I guess I can take solace in the fact that at least I gave it a shot—I tossed my hat in the ring. The committee just chucked the hat back at me, that's all. I'm sure I'll get a lot more hats thrown back at me throughout my life.

As far as the paintings entered, some had a major *Blue Taco* slant to them, while others were definitely on the *Self* side. One painting had Cesar Chavez wearing a Dodgers hat with the Virgin Mary tattooed on his chest, and another painting was just a blank canvas with a blue dot in the middle.

As bad as my two paintings were, though, they were still better than at least ten other paintings in the contest. I wonder if they were counting on their fellow Mexicans to turn in crappy paintings or missing the deadline to win, like I was.

I'd guess there were some forty-five paintings entered, so based on my calculations-*I came in thirty-fifth place, baby.*

And who knows? Maybe the best painting didn't win because it wasn't entered. That'd mean, technically, that my painting was better than theirs, because at least I entered the contest—I got thirty-fifth place, whereas they didn't even compete. At least that's the way I'm going to look at it.

I won the Twenty-Second Annual Max Edward's Free Throw Shooting Contest in seventh grade based on similar circumstances.

Max Edward was a special-needs student who didn't do anything but shoot free throws at school. He couldn't read, write, or speak, but he could shoot and make free throws all day long. He was kind of a savant, but with free throws, not with a piano or violin.

Everyone knew Lino Vasquez was the best basketball player in the school. Everyone knew he could win the free throw contest with his eyes shut. On the day of the contest, though, he didn't show up. The gym was empty when me and five other kids entered the gym. Mr. Ring, the gym teacher, thought we had entered the contest, so he tossed us a basketball ball and told us to get to the free throw line.

The five of us looked around, and when we didn't see Lino Vasquez anywhere, we ran onto the court. I only made four out of ten shots, but it was good enough to be proclaimed the Twenty-Second Annual Max Edward's Free Throw Shooting Champion at Imperial Junior High School. It's even documented—page 57 in the yearbook shows me holding my trophy, the same trophy that's still on my bedroom dresser. *Oh, yeah, baby*!

Speaking of "throwing my hat in the ring," I've decided to give stand-up another shot. This time, however, I'm going to stack the deck in my favor—I figure I need a "Blue Taco" crowd in the audience for me to be successful, so I'm going to print some flyers saying it's *"Raza Night,"* or "Bring One Cousin, the Second Cousin Gets in Free Night."

I'll stick the flyers up in the LBSA office, the MEChA office, the Student Health Center, the E.O.P. office, the financial aid office, the bus stop in front of the university, on the windshields of all the cars parked outside of the parking lot, and, just so I won't be accused of racial profiling, I'll put a flyer on the Chemistry Club's bulletin board.

I'm also throwing my hat in the ring regarding a poetry contest sponsored by the English Department. That's the good thing about having ADD, I guess—I find myself trying many different things. My condition drives my family and friends nuts, but I prefer to view my ADD as "God's natural energy drink."

None of my poems have titles, but I'll come up with them later—just like I did with the paintings. A maximum of two poems can be submitted, so I must narrow the following down.

~ the robber killed her before
she could commit suicide,
her parents slept better

~ the radio is on, she
dances in the night, he
died on the way home

~ playing basketball alone in
the dark, a car turns into the
driveway, playing basketball
alone in the dark

~ the rich man's, the poor
man's, it all goes down the
drain

I don't have any delusions of winning this contest, but what the hell? I might as well give it a shot. My tío Ricardo always says that good things will eventually happen to those who are persistent.

My tío Ricardo believes this because he's living proof that there's a payoff at the end for those who never give up. He should know—he got caught fourteen times by immigration before making it across the border on his fifteenth attempt.

Everyone kept telling him that he should drop at least 40 pounds before trying to jump a fence, cross a desert, and run from Border Patrol agents, but he was stubborn—he thought his fat-ass could waddle into el norte unscathed.

He's my dad's youngest brother, and although they're very close now-they went years without speaking to each other.

My mom told me that when my tío Ricardo finally made it to La Habra, he stayed with them for a few weeks. The problems started when my tío Ricardo would take off in my father's car without permission. That'd piss my dad off because my tío Ricardo didn't have a driver's license, much less car insurance. My father was worried that if my uncle got into a car accident and hit someone, they'd sue my father, since he owned the car, and go after all of his government cheese in the fridge or something.

Finally, one day they had a big falling out and my uncle moved out of the house and didn't talk to my dad for years. My uncle didn't even invite my dad to his wedding—that's how mad he was at my father.

Turns out, illegal aliens coming to the United States don't just get white people from Iowa and Texas pissed off and frustrated—they cause a lot of drama with their own legal families already in the United States.

I know many Mexican-Americans who wish the government would build a big-ass wall along the border to keep out all of the drama that comes over from their "visiting" relatives.

140

There's even drama in my family. My cousin, Chuyita, is mad at my parents because they won't let her use my sister's Social Security number to get a job at the local Burger King as a cook. Chuyita really wants the job, too, because she loves Burger King french fries. Now, who in the hell *loves* Burger King's french fries? McDonald's, Del Taco, and In-and-Out fries, I can understand—but *Burger King french fries*?

This drama isn't anything compared to what I read about the other day—an illegal alien dude killed his cousin, an American citizen, because she wouldn't set him up on a date with any of her friends. The guy wanted to marry an American citizen so he wouldn't be deported back to Mexico. He got part of his wish: He does get to stay in California the rest of his life—but in San Quentin State Penitentiary.

After the reception that was held for the contest, we all removed our paintings from the wall and took them home. I tossed mine in the trunk and headed off to Tavo's Cave. I was going to stop by Ollie's liquor store to buy some Doritos, but I didn't even make it out of the parking lot—I ran out of gas.

I didn't want to call anyone at Tavo's Cave for help because they'd just laugh at my ass and probably not even help me out anyway. I knew nobody from LBSA was around because they were all at a big "Minorities in the Business World" conference trying to get internships. I definitely wasn't going to call my dad because he'd give me the hardest time of all—he's always preaching about how one should always have at least half a tank of gas in the car at all times.

I was going to have to bail my own ass out of this situation, so I started walking toward the Chevron gas station on St. College and Commonwealth.

The gas station didn't have any gas cans, so I bought a gallon of Arrowhead water, poured it out, and filled it back up with gas. I then looked through the trash can, and took an empty 16-ounce Pepsi plastic bottle back with me to the car.

When I got back, I cut off the bottom part of the Pepsi bottle and placed the cap end in the gas tank. Next, I poured the gallon of gas through the Pepsi bottle and into the tank. And just like that, I was on my way. I spilled gas on my pants, so I headed home to change before going to The Cave.

As I was driving home, I realized that I had something in common with my father and his compadres—I, too, was a carrier of the Mexican Engineering Gene.

Actually, there's a lot of creativity and ingenuity involved with Mexican Engineering. I honestly think that if my dad got together with about five of his compadres and nobody bugged them for a week, they'd be able to figure out how the Egyptians built the pyramids—I think today's archeologists are overthinking their theories.

Once I got home, I took the painting inside and hung it above my bed, next to the huge crucifix an aunt had given me years ago, an old faded Sports Illustrated swimsuit calendar, a Mexican flag, a poster of the Pittsburg Steelers and the *Self* **painting I had put there earlier**. I must admit, *Flying Blue Tacos* looked like it had been hanging there for years—it blended in perfectly.

As I was leaving the bedroom, I could've sworn I heard Jesus, while hanging on the cross, let out an "*Órale*" regarding the *Blue Taco* painting.

I quickly turned around hoping to see His approval, but Jesus didn't say a word—He just kept looking at me with His bloody stoic face, as if saying, "*What*?"

At least he didn't say "*Chale*," I thought to myself as I left the room.

So, with Jesus mad-dogging me, and I don't mean *Jesús Martinez* from apartment D-6, I went downstairs to eat a *taco de bologna*—my dad's specialty, and another example to put on the "Taco list," not that I'll ever bother making such a list again.

142